CW00695467

For more information contact:
info@thebalance.rehab

First edition September 2022

ISBN 978-3-907427-00-2 (paperback)
ISBN 978-3-033-08979-2 (ebook)
ISBN 978-3-033-09436-9 (audiobook)

www.thebalance.rehab

LIVING
A LIFE IN
BALANCE

ABDULLAH BOULAD

THANK YOU FOR PURCHASING THIS BOOK

If you would like to know more about Abdullah's luxury rehab clinic where he practices the methods contained in this book with his clients, you can visit the website here:

www.thebalance.rehab

A portion of the proceeds from the book will be donated to Ukrainians displaced by the conflict.

If you would like to be notified about the release of the audiobook that is coming very soon for Living a Life in Balance (and future publications from The Balance) please head over to the website below and enter your email.

www.thebalance.clinic/livingalifeinbalancebook

For any questions about the book, Abdullah or The Balance luxury rehab clinic, don't hesitate to reach out.

info@thebalance.rehab

" إلى أولادي ، أرجو أن تنظروا إلى كلماتي ،و"
" تشعرون بالإرث الذي أسعى إلى منحكم إياه "

"To my children, may you look upon my words,
and feel the legacy I seek to bestow upon you"

TABLE OF CONTENTS

Introduction 1

A Few Years Back, and Some History to Boot.................1
Why This Book? Where Did It All Start? 5
The Partitioning 18

Physical Health 21

Food. Food. Food..28
What is nutrition? The Scientific Part...............................31
Proteins – the masons of your body 33
Carbohydrates: Not the Enemy..36
OMG! Fats! 38
Vita-mania and the Supplement Craze 42
The Human Microbiome..47
Ups & Downs, Breakthroughs and Discovery................50
Fad Diets 57
What's best for you, works for you!..................................59
Your Fitness...61
Deep Sleep 76
The Art of Creating a Lifestyle 85
Routines, Routines, Routines 86
Neuroplasticity: Exceptional Ability to Learn Faster.....95

Mental Health 101

I refuse The Autopilot Mode 102
Your Mind: The Useful Thinking Tool............................105
Mindfulness: Connection to The Present 110
Debunking Meditation 116
Purpose, Vision, Passion..121
Relationship with Limiting Beliefs 129
Act When You Should 137
Gratitude and Awe..140
The Key to Love Yourself..144

Social Health..**149**

    Meaningful Connections 149

    On Loneliness and Depression......................... 152

    When Life Happens.. 156

    The COACH within 165

    On Friends & Empathy...................................... 178

Spiritual Health..**186**

    The Lost and Found; Soul 188

    Consciousness is Silence.................................... 195

    The Good Place.. 199

    Resilience: Mastering Life 209

    Optimism.. 217

    Time and Death.. 224

    Acceptance 244

Final Thoughts **257**

INTRODUCTION

A Few Years Back, and Some History to Boot

I was born in Lebanon. To those who do not know what Lebanon is and where it is located, open any map, look for that square-ish expanse of water called the Mediterranean Sea, trace your finger a little to the right – opposite Cyprus – and you'll find a little spot of land, peculiarly shaped; elongated, flaring from the bottom up, a little like a miniature Portugal. It is a beautiful little spot of land, artfully located on the eastern coast of Mediterranean Sea and has always been regarded as the gate to the East. Lebanon is mostly dominated by two massive parallel mountain ranges embracing the Beqaa valley inland to the east, while a superb coast stretches over roughly two hundred and twenty kilometers. It is truly a miniature world in such a way that it has everything, from beautiful scenery, buzzing nightlife, amazing weather, to bustling cities.

A few thousand years ago, my ancestors, the Phoenicians, made the universal discovery of the written word; the alphabet. At the time, this newborn innovation was regarded with great, but simple excitement. It was a breakthrough from the ancestral ways of trade; the earliest form of disruption that put Phoenician on top of the trade food chain. In other words, they could record everything in minute detail and keep the data for ulterior use. It was a stroke of genius! Little did they know that this set of symbols will later alter the world. Little did they know that they would forever change the course of history, lest extend their reach into Celtic territory. The power within was released. The magic of the human mind – not the egoic one, can now be literally set in stone, written on paper, even tattooed on your skin. The magic they had released onto the world can be either light or dark, and humans can master both; it's a matter of conscious choice, bolstered by all that your subconscious has engulfed, recorded, devoured, and digested since you took your first breath. Phoenicians sought to trade – mostly – and expand their market; others conspired and used the magic of the spoken and written word to invoke the worst in humans; malevolence and mal-intent. Phoenician cities, which were not really equipped to sustain warfare, were hammered with attacks. This population of traders was skilled in masonry and carpentry, but war was not their *forte*. The alphabet they had created helped set powers in motions that were beyond their understanding. And, as it is with all inventions that were the product of good intentions, the application that ensued was not close to the original intended one. Allow me to elaborate; wider more intent on dissecting that power and using it for their benefit were able to smash lesser opponents, expand their knowledge and manipulate time itself. This unknown power had started to be tamed. Think in terms of worldwide conflicts, personal strife, and psychological ailments to say the least. The word is power, and power is a double-edged sword; it is addictive, clear, yet confusing if not taken seriously.

Case in point, I was born and raised there amid the horrific civil war – in 1979 – to a father who was a frequent traveler with keen eyes and a sharp mind and a warm-hearted mother. I remember sitting around the kitchen table for breakfast, my small legs swinging, not even touching the floor, my mother serving us fresh vegetables and olives; oh! Those gorgeous green and black olives were a sight for sore eyes, their taste was beyond anything I have and will ever taste anywhere in the world! I remember people running from house to house, their shuffling feet heard in the frightening silence, nervously knocking on doors looking for missing relatives, siblings, parents, and friends. I remember the booming noises of explosions near and far, I recall my father handing his shield to a friend of his, I can even evoke memories of footage broadcast on the television, the intonation of news anchors reading the news bulletin and the jingle of the AM news stations on the radio. There was urgency to their tone. Yet, they tried to keep their voices level not knowing where and when a building might crumble.

Reflecting on the seven years that I had spent in my war-torn country; numerous realizations hit me right in the face. I am a man whose inner child had, and still is, carrying within the confines of its subconscious the weight of a missed childhood.

We are sponges, children, and adults alike, and we are the products of our own environment(s), of the words used around us, of the magic that others invoke. We share common feelings and are all connected through the power of our brains. Our thoughts course through neurons vibrating and letting out rippling energy that recognizes neither distance nor time. The reality we tend to overlook is that we are frequency generators and receivers, which either makes us powerful or apathetic or merely weak. My short history and experience with the Lebanese civil war still clings to my very core. Even though I was still a child at the time, and that I did not directly partake in the happenings right outside our door; the frequencies, thoughts, actions, and words around me slashed at my young self like razors. I still bear the scars. I am proud of them.

As I have mentioned earlier, I have made realizations and breakthroughs, and I want to share with you some intimate details of my life throughout this book. These memories and thoughts will serve as an anchor point as we progress together. This is your journey moving in parallel with mine, and I will be walking along with you as we evolve, unlearn, and learn anew. You'll see your own footprints in the sand upon looking back what your efforts; you'll notice how much stronger you have become as you break the chains of what has been forcefully implanted in your mind.

In this book, you will find a 360 view of the amazing creatures humans are. I will put my knowledge at your disposal, from the scientific to the spiritual. All you must do is open your body and mind to the energy I am sharing with you. It is a simple process. It is a complicated process. You choose. You control your reality, and with this supremacy over other creatures, you can dictate what you want and manifest your innermost desires. The universe will not judge you; it is energy, pure and simple.

"Ask and it shall be given to you" Matthew 7:7–8

Why This Book? Where Did It All Start?

The words in this book stem from my willingness to be part of a change, little be it or significant in your life. I want you to delve into the truth behind this publication and find yourself saying, *"He was here, he wrote truth."* The words I want to leave hanging and ringing in your ears are those of a man who lived a life that is rich in experiences, a life that he *enriched* with experiences.

The current level of awareness and conscious living I have reached did not come easily. Therefore, I poured all that I am into this book. My hope is that this blueprint will help you find your true self, tap into your true nature, and comprehend the importance of being truly connected. My transformative journey started upon getting into that car, kneeling on the wide back seat, and looking at my grandparent's waving goodbye in tears. I saw my family being ripped apart. It felt necessary to my parents, it felt unfair to me, but I was a simple bystander in the process. My emotions were a jumble of electrical signals that I did not grasp, and all I could recognize was the pain of being torn away from what felt like a group of warm, typically loud and generous Lebanese relatives. Strong feelings can be uncomfortable, but not being able to understand those boiling little things was just overwhelming. Truth be told, I still cling to their image in my mind until they became a blur. Maybe from the distance, maybe from my own tears, maybe from the many times I conjured up this scene in my head until it became fuzzy and unclear.

The next thing I knew is that we had reached Switzerland. I was seven years old at the time; a child that carried a heavy load of psychological baggage. It felt as if my body was overburdened and chained by the shelling back in Lebanon, the sporadic war crimes, the feeling that nothing was permanent, not even my own self. I stepped into peaceful Switzerland with war still raging inside my mind. It was not my war *per se*, but the loud explosions and the general feeling of unease felt so very deeply entrenched into my constitution that leading a quiet life had become an alien concept. In Lebanon, war had been normalized; a mistake that can be repaired through self-mastery and self-compassion, which is part of why I wrote this book.

I used to wake up in this new country to the sound of blasts shaking the house. But were they real? Definitely not! Yet, the baggage I was carrying around with me felt so real. The illusion that I was still under siege, locked up in my own house and not being able to step outside to play was vivid, so vivid!

There was darkness inside, a sort of obscurity that was stagnant and churning. But I felt I could manage to divide this dark entity and conquer it. This was the first thing I did. I could not live with another entity poisoning my system. As a growing child, I did not have enough power or understanding to express what I had just described, but it did feel like a board game. This is how my mind's eye perceived my situation; a game that I had to win.

As time went by, Beirut became a faded image, like one of those Polaroid pictures. It was the flat and gray image of a country that was once flourishing and then forcefully plunged into the abyss of war, hatred, and destruction. Lebanon became the exact image of a dysfunctional mind that is at war with itself.

My first attempt at banishing this dark entity was not fruitful due to my sole lack of knowledge and awareness. How could I dissect that which I was not equipped to understand? I was faced with an additional stack of stressors to my peers; I was in a different country, a wholly different context. I was oblivious to the language and to the culture. I used to live in Beirut. It was vibrant, alive, loud, and almost musical; neighbors invited each other spontaneous over for coffee and meals, roads were packed with bustling bodies, cars, shops, and pubs. The reality I was planted in was the exact opposite of what I used to; our apartment near Zurich was very tranquil. Akin to any other kid, I had expectations, or at least *wanted* Zurich to be the comforting place that looked like the Lebanese capital. Those expectations were simple associations with scenes from movies, books, even fairy tales where everyone was simply happy. I expected to see loads of people interacting with each other, but all I got was beautiful vista of a gorgeous city as still as a painting. That discrepancy hit me hard, and I experienced my first cultural jolt. Zurich was the polar opposite of Beirut.

Before our migration, I was a very good student. In fact, I was a great student; I excelled in all subjects and even managed to leap a scholastic year. I felt that aura fade away as I stepped into my first ever class in Switzerland. Insecurities slammed into me igniting fears that I had seldom felt or not yet encountered. These were inwardly directed fears; fears of failure and rejection, fears originating from the lack of understanding of my direct environment. I was not afraid of the people or the places I was frequenting. I was scared to the core of my own situation; me being alien to this culture. In other words, I was the other who was not able to communicate with his peers, and with the lack of communication – the lack of the power of the spoken word – I was left alone, even rudely treated by other children. To the simple and innocent eyes of my peers, I was the little, dark Muslim standing in contrast to the Swiss Christian status quo. It was a conflicting idea to many who did not understand or accept the fact that I was beyond what they were seeing. My parents also had their share of that adaptation stress. I could see sadness washing over them as they tried to learn the language, manage the house, work, and keep everything running as though nothing had changed. But everything *had* changed, and we couldn't overlook its impact on our household. This whole equation of us being of Muslim background in a majority Christian country, being forced out of our homeland and not fitting the locals' expectations set another gray veil over our new reality. I grew lonely at times, feeling isolated and chained by my past irrational fears and insecurities regarding my identity.

When I say I was not afraid of the people around me, I mean that I had a somewhat simplistic understanding that this was a different place not torn by warring militias. There was no fear of physical attacks, none of the students in my class could relate to the resilience that the Lebanese possess in the face of adversity. What were militias to my eyes then? They were evil and greedy entities destroying everything in their wake. It was like in one of those fairy tales where children had to run across the dark woods to escape for their lives, evading villains and making do with what they had, only I did not have a trail to lead me back to safety because there was no place to go back to; *I was* the dark woods as well as the children running through them.

This idea when merged with my current knowledge, finally for me illuminated the contagious nature of that the darkness that was spreading in Lebanon.

I was fortunate enough to be brought up with a resilient sense of self-esteem, and as I went through the process of adaptation, which took some time, I started to understand much of how the world was at work. It rendered me more flexible, provided me with human and humane assets, and tools to subtly dissect the words and actions I was subjected to. My upbringing, my past and the future I was trying to visualize merged to create a whole new sense of self allowing me to become empathetic. Even though I had stopped thinking about my past and was focused on the *now*, I sensed a pressing sensation to achieve even more. I was living different realities, parallel realities. I could almost see those realities with my own eyes, which were still not very well equipped to comprehend. But my intuition; the voice emanating from within my being told me different stories were at play.

As time went by, school and after-school time became somewhat traumatic. I was the outsider, the "dark" little boy who couldn't properly communicate with others, the outsider that was not able to learn proper German, the outsider that did well in math, but would probably not get to go into what they call the *Gymnasium*.

A tiny explanation is due here for readers from outside of Northern Europe: The Gymnasium is nothing close to the gym that you are familiar with; in fact it is not related to fitness in any way. Students who wanted an academic career sought to enter what is called the *Mittelschule* or *Kantonsschule*, which would prepare them for the *Matura* at the age of 18 or 19.

The breakthrough happened just after the time when my teacher looked at my grades and, to my dismay, refused to allow me into the Gymnasium. Teachers, at this point, were entitled to decide whether the student could get into the higher or lower secondary school or not, which also meant that I, given my GPA, needed my teacher's approval. The decision was not unexpected; I knew deep inside that his verdict was already negative on the sole grounds that I was different. With my teenage mind totally unphased nor allowing me to be dampened by this setback, I began to push my limits and go the extra mile in everything I did. I admit, at that age, I did feel as though I was downgraded, as though I was not deserving of a shiny academic career, of a beautiful life or of the bright future that seemed almost promised to my peers. But it was also a trigger for me to contest this view and correct it.

Take my story as perhaps, an opportunity to draw your attention to what is a fabrication and what is reality. The most manifested unconscious human behavior is that of racism and the assumption of mal intent. You can paint any image in your mind. You are the artist painting reality. But here's the catch, you need to be aware that once you are trespassing in other people's thoughts by assuming that they are attacking you, or simply being negative, you are indeed creating such a reality. Your behavior will shift towards that end, and eventually you will reach a point where you will say "I knew it!".

Let me gently break it to you; you know nothing, I know nothing, nobody truly knows anything. You only manifested it because you firmly believed that you will be the victim, not because others are evil, not because they regard you as a lesser human being. You made it happen because you perhaps think yourself beneath everybody else. What is even worse, is that you had no doubt about it! You claimed knowledge as dictated by your own mind, let the poison spread through your system and allowed your mind – again – to blame others for your personal downs. Look inwardly, love yourself; relinquish the tyrannical thoughts that plague your Being.

Relinquish your mind altogether and step out into the light of your Being. The light is a step away and requires only acceptance, pure and simple acceptance. Let go of societal presets, the "I felt so," as well as your mind's *shortcuts* that are only applicable to you and you will find that once the "philosopher" inside opens his/her eyes to the truth, you will accept everybody else the way you accept yourself (given that you accept and love yourself unconditionally).

Going back to my story, I can tell you that after being rejected, my brain and being, as opposed to my mind, experienced what you call in French a "déclic" or "wake up call". It was the first step towards the light. I started absorbing information and knowledge at a rapid pace. I began to morph into the successful individual that I thought could be the answer to all my problems. However, skepticism always held constancy in my mind, and I wondered if this new persona was the one that I wanted, or whether it was the image that my new society was trying to force upon me.

I wondered if I still carried around the image of the successful, smart little child that is to become a doctor, architect, or lawyer as dictated by my Lebanese roots. We all tend to hear comments of such nature during our childhoods, we all are *given* the stereotype seed, and are brainwashed into accepting images of ourselves as portrayed by the needs of adults seeking to orient us towards what they *think* is right. The process of domestication is not really as we see with cats and dogs; it is much worse; it goes much deeper than just having a child act the way we see fit. Domestication came as the product of us judging our "naturally behaving" animal counterparts as being savage or wild. The idea of civility as discussed since antiquity was based on the idea that we are above every other creature that roams this earth. Yet, I would like to question this concept. Are we really being above animals by dressing ourselves and behaving in a certain way or simply countering what nature has integrated into our being in terms of intuition, natural tendencies, and aptitudes?

Are we really that limited? Am I only to become a doctor? Is being an architect really the definition of who I really am? We are part of something way bigger, our *selves* are us being our own truths, and being our own truths is way larger than life; the life we are taught to see through limiting filters. Throughout this book, I seek to provide you with enough tools to reach self-mastery. I seek to provide you with the *sight* and with that ability see through the dreadful opaque fabric of false reality as dictated by society and even the whole planet.

Despite my scholastic setback, I was not discouraged and looked for opportunities. The era of computers was kicking off and I wanted to be right at the center; I wanted to experiment and prove to myself that I was enough, more than enough. Without giving up hope, I started buying computer parts, assembling desktop computers, and selling them. I became a self-taught "business-teen" and experimented with

Atari and Commodore 64. I became an entrepreneur, not just a young man with a drive. Surely at that time, I was merely following my intuition, enjoying the little successes, and allowing my knowledge to expand without labeling the process. But come to think of it, things were on the right track thanks to the rejection I experienced, and to being that little outsider who had to break many of the shackles of his past. I am thankful and proud of my former self for accepting rejection. By accepting rejection, I had partially muted my mind and focused on what can be done now. This was the beginning of my separation with the poisonous over-thinker that was crippling me. I wanted to access the Gymnasium, but I shifted my energy to investing into my own development and being my own boss.

At the age of sixteen I started studying Architecture Design and was running my web design company in parallel. I had garnered so much experience that by the age of twenty I underwent the Matura and kicked off my studies at university. I admit, it was difficult, I had so many responsibilities, and the only gratification I had was the prospect of reaching my ultimate self. I could visualize an older version of me being successful and making change. To my mind's eye, I wanted to make a ripple in time and leave something of worth.

My life's journey so far has been one of great experiences, regardless of whether they are depicted as ups or downs – no judgment here. This text originated from the fact that I needed to provide you with some sort of flexible and relatable blueprint. I will be contesting your *limiting beliefs* that stereotype much of our understanding of reality, I will also shed light on the importance of faith, religious or not, in awakening the inner *Observer*. We are all blessed with the ability to see; *truly* see how this world functions.

The source of all the information in this is piece of work and the legitimacy backing it up stem from the real-life stories that will intersperse the thoughts and concepts I will be explaining as we journey together. They will act as a reference and inspiration. My journey that led me to my current state will also be evident through my way of expression. I am willing to make myself vulnerable and available for examination. You are invited to take whatever is good for you and make it work according to what the truth requires from you. When I say truth, I mean the unwavering reality that you are; the reality that is palpable and your own presence that needs no evidence or acknowledgement. You are the truth and only you can tap into it. I will be providing in this book a set of little screwdrivers that will allow you to open the lid into your existence, dust off all that has been poured in, clean up the parts, and emerge new and rejuvenated. The key is to unlearn all that we thought was correct, and objectively regard reality.

"We know more than we think,
and we think more than we know"

Introduction

This is an invitation to health, wellbeing, and inner balance. You might wonder why I would mention health and wellbeing together here. In many instances, those two terms were used interchangeably, and as is the case with many technical terms out there, the nuances are being lost due to overuse. However, I feel compelled to make sure you know the difference as you have taken the initiative to pick up this book. It's a good thing you did! I hope you will feel the care and genuine attention to your needs that I have put behind these words. Furthermore, you will notice how everything will look interconnected as we all are.

Health is having a positive and optimistic outlook with the sense that you are in control of your life. This includes the ability to relax, maintain a good level of energy, enjoying the support of a balanced social network and a satisfying job or endeavor. Wellbeing is *choosing* to live your life in an enjoyable way to reach your potential. It is the ability to consciously know that you *can* and have the right to be happy and healthy, which also includes taking action to do so. My aim is to make you your own guru and to give you all the tools at my disposal so that you could integrate your body's, mind's and spirit's processes/needs in the most balanced way. Acknowledging the vital importance of upholding your health and wellbeing, as well as knowing what works for you will make a huge difference in terms of developing your healthier sense of self, unlearning society's limiting beliefs and allowing your true self to shine through.

17

The Partitioning

If I have to describe this book, I would most certainly view it as a pyramid that encompasses all that is of prominence for your progress into a healthier lifestyle. This pyramid starts with physical health at the base, moves up to Mental Health, Social Health, and finally Spiritual Health. The path I have drawn, as seen in the illustration below, will eventually lead you to the ultimate form of healthy living and towards something that is of a higher significance, self-mastery.

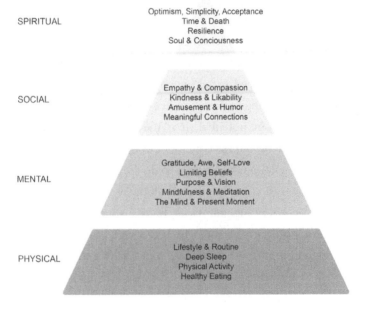

SPIRITUAL

Optimism, Simplicity, Acceptance
Time & Death
Resilience
Soul & Conciousness

SOCIAL

Empathy & Compassion
Kindness & Likability
Amusement & Humor
Meaningful Connections

MENTAL

Gratitude, Awe, Self-Love
Limiting Beliefs
Purpose & Vision
Mindfulness & Meditation
The Mind & Present Moment

PHYSICAL

Lifestyle & Routine
Deep Sleep
Physical Activity
Healthy Eating

I have chosen to start with the simplest yet most vital elements. The base of the pyramid and the first sections of this book will provide you with all information to upkeep your body, nourish it and sustain it physically since having a healthy body is one of your tools to tame the mind and mute its opportunistic attempts.

You might have already been exposed to similar information from a variety of sources, so I want to make sure to remind you of the little things that make a huge difference. This pyramid is the illustration of what will lead you to living a life in balance. We are all fundamentally alike, we are all carriers of cosmic energy and can wield it to our hearts' desires, for it neither judges nor sets conditions. The only requirement is faith in your *Being*. Once you start looking at your physical self and loving it, your soul will be at ease and the overthinker - your mind – will retreat into the corner. You will have started the detachment process.

From the moment we take our first breath up until we let go of our last, mastering oneself requires you to relinquish doubt and skepticism as they will hinder your progress. I, therefore, ask you to read this book objectively, make pauses and reflect on your journey so far; on the thought processes that have led you to places you wanted to be or didn't want to reach, on the causes behind some of your decisions, on the feelings that you have experienced and the way you dealt with them. I advise you to read this book keeping in mind that I have crafted my sentences in such a way as to give you space to break your generational curses.

By being objective with yourself you will allow you to fully fathom the greatness that you have within. You and I are human, true! But we have so much more to offer to this universe than just existing. You are entitled to greatness; all you must do is look in the fine print. You are bigger than you think, you are larger than life and destined to receive the blessings of the universe only if you truly have faith in the energy coursing through you.

PHYSICAL HEALTH

The umbrella that encompasses all that I will be talking about in this book can be summed up under Healthy Lifestyle. A lifestyle does not require you to spend money on spa treatments, vacations, and entertainment. On the contrary, it is going back to yourself and to your inner child. What I would like you to experience is the beautiful feeling that is born out of enjoying your body in its current shape and loving it, contributing to your community, expanding your consciousness, developing empathy, or if you already are on that path, further provide it with tools to get closer to the divine you.

What does the body have to do with the divine? I know that it animates the body, but can you elaborate on that idea? It seems too scientific to include any kind of spiritual connection.

Without a properly nurtured body, you will not have enough room to tackle all remaining obstacles and fight your demons. You will have to start with your body since it is the most tangible of things and once you start becoming healthier, your mood will change allowing you to be the best version of yourself. I do not mean that you have follow the media's beauty criteria, but follow that which suits you, practice what physically and mentally strengthens you. Have you ever gone so long without food that you suddenly experienced mood swings? We usually and non-scientifically refer to it as being "hangry". Have you ever exercised too much that you ended up, not only sore, but also sick and irritable? This is what we call overtraining. I can ask you a million questions and you would probably answer most of them with "*yes!*"

This book has various parts that I have crafted in a way to cater to your specific needs and to your internal constitution. The first part of this book will be simply scientific information about nutrition, because being human is enjoying all that life has to offer, and I have come to love food and have developed a great rapport with it. With that healthy relationship with food, I have discovered its extensive impact on the body and thought processes. It is crucial for you and for me to start right here with what makes us tick on the physiological level. To be perfectly honest, food has always been important to me ever since I was a child. We all have a peculiar relationship with what we ingest, and coming from a Lebanese background, food has always played an important role on the personal and social fronts. We eat when we are happy, we eat when we are grieving, and we eat when we have nothing else to do. But the best part of our food is that it is the healthiest around the world. You must have heard about the Mediterranean diet; it is not a diet *per se*, but a lifestyle that relies on eating seasonal and fresh products.

Thinking about food does not only make us happy or hungry, but most of us experience what being *"hangry"* feels like. It is not a joke when someone is battling hunger. This is our body notifying us to recharge it; that rumbling sound your stomach makes is calling you to take action; correct action. To simplify and perhaps make more "digestible" some of the more complex information I have garnered over the years, I can tell you that nutrition; this relatively new discipline, shares many common points with the topics I will be discussing later. Our bodies are universes in motion, and we are much weaker without proper nutrition. Give this organic machine of yours healthy food, and it flourishes, becomes more efficient, and with that you can reach clarity of mind, allowing your spirit to take center stage right before your own Being. It is not by chance that I have gone into the history of my people and delved deep into their nutritional habits, which have been shaped by their direct environment, needs and activities.

23

With that being said, I cannot but shift into the more serious impact of food on the human psyche. Apart from being quite the enjoyable ritual, food is the first and most abused "drug" since the dawn of time. It is a constant need that spikes periodically or sporadically forcing us to open the fridge in modern time, or to hunt in ancient ones. I had mentioned that it was not a joke when someone is hungry, and that statement also demonstrates how strong a hold food has on us. Our ancient ancestors would chase a prey for hours to satiate their hunger, walk miles to reach a river to quench their thirst. The only difference nowadays is that consuming food has leapt from being a necessity to a luxury drug that has led to a plethora of illnesses.

Wouldn't it be because our ancestors would die
without food and most importantly without water?

True! That is correct! However, humans have evolved into machines that only need to consume. If hunting, gathering, and looking for clean water were survival needs, what these needs have mutated into has drifted away from the idea of fulfilling basic needs. We are beings of extremes, and you see that everywhere, from apparel to architecture and even to showing off how spiritual we are. I am not saying that we should not eat, and that starvation is something to be accepted. On the contrary, my vision is one of harmony, prosperity, and abundance. Yet, we have lost what it means to live in *moderation.*

Moderation is the concept to live by, and I shall be repeating it over and over again. When we step outside the moderation frame, the human brain becomes numb to the simpler pleasures of life. In today's world, where everything is readily available, humans tend to forget the beauty of awaiting the harvest of seasonal fruits, vegetables, nuts, and seeds. Ultimately, what we are going through is an age ravaged by greed; one that is fueled by growing needs that are fundamentally wants in nature. The choice to live a moderate and healthy lifestyle stems from the awareness that we are living in a world that provides anything and everything attractive to the mind and body. Once you have this information downloaded into your system, you will become aware of how your choices dictate your future self, physically and mentally.

The moment you decide to break the chains of nonchalance regarding your own body is the moment your healing starts. Self-mastery and living in balance start with the decision to control a very visceral urge, appetite. Most of us take what we ingest into our bodies ever so lightly. That midnight snack you devoured, just because you have a sweet tooth or that bag of chips that you munched on while watching a film or series can easily be exchanged for healthier alternative or no alternative at all.

You need to understand that your mind acts on its own and produces needs that are virtual in nature. What I mean by virtual is that we are mostly weak before the appetite because we confuse it with real hunger. The mind plays tricks on the body, throwing virtual feelings and sensations; you then fall prey to these mirages, believe them and feed the illusion. Watch yourself and be aware of those recurring feelings.

Since we are the products of our environments, our wants and needs can easily be linked to the people around us, to habits that we have formed as children, enforced, and reinforced as time goes by. These habits, simple as they may sound, are behind much of our slip ups. We tell ourselves, "I have done well today, I deserve that bar of chocolate," "I am exhausted, I need that sugar," "a handful of candy won't kill me," "I am craving a hamburger with some fries."

You deserve to enjoy a nice reward! That is an uncontestable truth. You have done well working hard. But what you are doing is allowing your mind to feed you lies about what you deserve or not. You have already been tamed enough and are being tamed and re-tamed as you go. My words might come as slap in the face, but we are housetrained just like any pet crawling around the house. The only difference is that we are taught to use our abilities to think and express ourselves as per society's set norms. We are housetrained, this is the word for it; rewarded for doing the right thing or punished for any wrongdoing. The poisonous habit of blindly following rules, customs and regulations are enforced and ingrained in us; that pure canvas that is our own being upon birth is tainted and forced to overthink.

If I am to illustrate what I am saying, I would have to go back to those classic cartoon scenes where the subject is torn between two voices, the angel, and the devil. You are none of those two. In fact, you are the camera or the observer watching those two control your every decision, you are the one looking down on that lesser entity that is controlling you. The mind is the lesser entity. Why? Because instead of supporting you it wants you to shrink your Being.

Going back to nutrition, respecting your body's needs; those real needs that are linked to physiological hunger, as opposed to mere appetite, is crucial.

Appetite is psychological in nature: a feeling that we need something to satisfy a craving. It is simply a desire to eat and can be brought about thanks to various emotional and psychological causes.

Real hunger is physiological in nature: having your stomach empty and your energy stores depleted due to the lowering of your glycogen stores and so on. Hunger is the balance between ghrelin (the hunger hormone) and leptin (the satiety hormone), a result of various physiological changes.

Ask yourself these few questions once your cravings kick in:

- Can I fit a whole hamburger into my stomach right now?
- Is my mind playing tricks on me?
- I have just had a good lunch, am I really hungry an hour later?

Your body is a beautiful structure, made of celestial substances, this might sound poetic, but we really are made of star-stuff as they say. Love it the way it is, feed it intuitively, and elevate its value as you cater to its needs with mindfulness and awareness.

Food. Food. Food

Food is a source of energy for your body. It is either eaten or drunk and has a plethora of benefits. Food assists the body in rebuilding itself. In other words, when I reiterate the saying "you are what you eat," I mean that your body is rebuilt and altered based on what you ingest. Good food will eventually have you looking healthy and radiant, while overeating or under-eating foods that are not nutritious will eventually have detrimental effects on your body and mental performance.

The impact of food is definitely a physiological one. But, just like any other organism, our brains and bodies communicate a lot more than we think. We are usually not aware of the conversation that is happening right within us, and we tend to take what food can do for granted. In other words, we focus on what our minds order us to have regardless of the quality (especially when hunger or when appetite strike).

> *"You're starving! Get anything!*
> *Just anything, I need my glucose!"*

If you ever decide to go shopping while you are hungry, you will most definitely grab anything that seems filling. In short, your choice will include calorie dense foods that beat the purpose of what we call proper nutrition. Your mind seeks immediate gratification and acts in a selfish way, forgetting that the body needs to feed on nutrient rich food. Haven't you experienced hunger and the sinful rush to get or order anything later? We all have! The only difference now is that you will do the effort of developing the habit of being mindful of carefully reading your mind's signs, taming it, and making sure that it does not slip up.

Food is crucial to sustain life; however, as we progress into the twenty-first century, our relationship with that which provides life has become a somewhat complexly masochistic, greed-driven one. As part of my professional life, I have seen so many individuals wreck their lives using what seemed to be an innocent dessert, or a delicious looking dish. And so, I started wondering:

> ◆ How many individuals around the world really make the same mistake?

- ♦ Why do they make such devastating choices?

Some would claim that the answer resides in our direct environment, but I do believe that it is high time we took a journey inward, to that part of our existence that has fallen prey to the stress of daily life, the naggings of the mind and the incessant painting and repainting of our image by those around us. Our parents come to us with a perception of who we are and how we look, the media shoves another image into our brains, our friends comment on how thin or fat we are.

- ♦ Take a moment to stop.
- ♦ Take a breath.
- ♦ Count to three.
- ♦ Slowly release that breath.

You are not who they think you are. You are what you are and what you choose to be. Perfection is not only relative; perfection is you being perfectly you, the absolute Being able to fathom and implement self-mastery. Perfection is when you let go of your mind's needles pressing against the Being because, if you look inwardly, you will see the truth that you are the one holding the needles, you are allowing yourself to cause that emotional pain. The journey leading to letting go of those needles can be tough. Yet here you are reading this book in search for an answer. This means that you are aware of the potential that you have and are willing to activate it. You are here to awaken the dormant you that is beautiful in every way.

Allow the warrior in you to awaken and fight off the mind's darkness; become a warrior of the light.

I shall not comment on the hectic life we are living and impact of false information on our lives. But I would like to point out that *we* have turned our lives into stressful ones. Let us not be hasty in blaming just about anything for our failures. Your mother did not leave that cake on the table to tease you, your colleague did not gift you a chocolate bar to fatten you up! In most stressful situations, we tend to allow our minds to wander through the thorns and upon feeling the stinging pain, we start nagging and playing the blame game. In this case, we start eating mindlessly; we consume without really seeing.

What is nutrition? The Scientific Part

Nutrition is all that you ingest and its impact on your body. Nutrition, as a discipline, covers food the moment you take a bite, up until it is fully digested and discarded. Nutrition concerns itself with nutrients and includes five macronutrients: water, carbohydrates, proteins, fats, minerals, and vitamins.

There are specific quantities that are to be ingested by the body to ensure good health and optimal fitness. It is a relatively new field that has witnessed a major reform in the 1980s with the advent of technology allowing us to fathom the inner processes of the digestive tract. When we speak nutrition, we also speak of the functions of food, starting with the physiological, such as providing energy, hence sustaining life by allowing the body to grow, up to the psychological and the way the excess and lack thereof impact the brain and everyday performance. Food becomes a part of us as it is broken down by our digestive tract consuming energy to provide energy. This process obviously happens so that we can carry out our usual activities. It is a beautiful cycle that delicately reposes on listening to our body's needs, knowing what works and what doesn't work for us, and developing healthy habits.

When I say that eating is a habit, this means that you are the one who either makes yourself gain weight, stay fit, or become underweight. Even though there are thousands of trending diets out there, nothing can beat the power of your own will (cliché I know, but it is true).

What most people fail to see is that they need to control their minds, not vice versa. You are properly equipped to live a healthy lifestyle if you allow your body, mind, and spirit to naturally communicate. In other words, when you think in terms of moderation, you consume enough carbohydrates to sustain all your activities, enough proteins to build and rebuild your muscles, enough fats to help your hormones function properly and absorb fat-soluble vitamins crucial for your wellbeing. There is no hocus pocus here, there are no miracle pills, no voodoo dolls to kill fat and no occult solutions to ward off heart problems. There is just one way, the solution summarized as this: learn to love yourself enough to respect yourself and fulfill your needs.

Proteins – the masons of your body

Proteins are the building blocks of your muscles. Without them your body cannot repair and rebuild itself. They provide you with 4 calories per gram and are digested slowly, which means that they will keep you satiated (feeling full) for longer. Imagine your body as a factory that breaks down proteins. Amino acids – the building blocks of proteins – are broken down to be distributed to the lean tissue, hair, nails, skin, your immune system and the production of certain enzymes and hormones.

There are around twenty-two amino acids found in numerous combinations in different foods, nine of them essential, meaning that they are not produced by the body and should be included in our diet. They can either be animal-based or plant-based and their impact on the body greatly depends on their quality. I am not talking about what would happen in the present or a few days after the consumption of proteins, rather on the long run.

What is the difference between
animal-based proteins and plant-based proteins?

Animal-based proteins, such fish, eggs, red meat, and white meat, are complete proteins and are great sources of essential amino acids, they are also rich in heme iron (heme meaning blood). Such proteins are crucial for girls and women, as their bodies do not store iron, in addition to being rich in vitamin B-12, zinc, phosphorus, creatine, riboflavin, niacin and thiamin. Their plant-based counterparts, such as beans, nuts, seeds, tofu are majorly incomplete sources of protein, but this does not stop them from playing a major role in our diet. Let me clarify, since various plants contain various amino acids, combining the right plant-based proteins together can assist in replacing some of the less healthy ones from the animal realm. Yet, as I have mentioned, it all goes back to your overall physical health and fitness level, which eventually will dictate your body's needs. There is a plethora of vegetarian and vegan recipes/diets that can help you shed those extra kilos. But the point here is not to simply lose weight, but to live a life that fits your body and your overall goals.

Then should I rely on animal-based proteins in my healthy diet?

You can in fact make complete proteins out of plant-based proteins. Let me illustrate this for you. My grandma used to make a delicious Lebanese lentil soup and hummus dip. As a kid I was encouraged to eat as much as I can since "lentils strengthen the knees," my grandma used to say, pouring me a second and sometimes a third. Watching the thick soup fill my plate, I always wondered why my grandmother would include rice. I did enjoy the taste and texture, but I did not understand the correlation between the two until I had the opportunity to delve into the science of nutrition.

It just so happens that lentils and rice complement each other to make quasi-complete proteins. The same applies to hummus and oat crackers, as well as other traditional Lebanese/Mediterranean dishes.

Bottom line, you can eat moderate amounts of high-quality proteins from a variety of sources; plant and animal-based to allow your body to recover and rebuild itself. When I say in moderation, this means that on average your body will require 0.8 grams of proteins per gram of bodyweight. These numbers obviously change depending on many variables such as, activity and fitness level, age, lean muscle mass, goals, and health status. Despite the recent studies that bash the previous correlations between cancer, type 2 diabetes, heart disease and other ailments with meat consumption, I would like to stress the importance of leafy greens, whole grains, milk and dairy products, alongside high-quality lean meats, and other heme-iron rich sources. In moderate quantities!

Carbohydrates: Not the Enemy

Carbohydrates (CHO) are essential for your body's energy needs. They provide you with 4 calories per gram; they can be found anywhere, from bread to vegetables. They are the primary fuel of both body and brain, but to many, carbs are the enemy and play the supporting role to proteins. Carbohydrates are so misunderstood that I feel the need to pinpoint their vital importance and their effect on the body.

Consuming carbs is vital for your muscles, but most importantly for your brain. Yet, as is the case with all other nutrients, not all carbs are created equal. With the advancement of technology, the food industry has provided us with so many "healthy" alternatives; processed carbohydrates, which are the focus of this section. These might be turned into glucose by our bodies with a hidden secondary effect.

We all know that natural unprocessed rolled oats, wholegrain bread and brown rice are rich in dietary fibers. This means that upon consumption and digestion, glucose is gradually released into the bloodstream, keeping insulin level at optimal levels, and refreshing your gut's microbiota; your body's team of good bacteria, archaea and fungi that live in your digestive tract. In other words, your body will be able to use said carbs and in certain situations tap into the adipose tissue to provide energy throughout long bouts of low-intensity workouts.

Carbohydrates have been set in a table called the Glycemic Index, which means that each source of CHO has a specific quantity of blood sugar it releases into the bloodstream. The higher the GI, the more/faster blood sugar is released, either spiking your insulin or allowing its slow release into the bloodstream.

Avoiding carbs altogether has detrimental effects on your body, which will have to break down proteins, mostly your muscle mass to maintain its energy level. Protein breakdown is very inefficient and will leave you tired, skinny-fat and most importantly irritable.

What is insulin in the first place?
What does it do? Doesn't it make me fat?

Insulin is a hormone produced by the body. Its function is of great importance; as our digestive tract breaks down proteins into amino acids, fats into fatty acids and carbohydrates into glucose. Insulin, produced by the pancreas, helps transport these nutrients into cells by literally acting as an usher; opening the cells' "gates."

I will not go into the full scientific descriptions of what happens, but you should know that once nutrients are absorbed into cells, insulin levels usually drop to what is called the "baseline level." Now, the ongoing story that insulin is your worst enemy has been labeled as a myth since you are responsible for your weight gain, not the hormone *per se*. There is some truth to the fact that insulin will keep on shuttling nutrients, including fatty acids, into cells and allowing them to expand. But this is not what causes fat to accumulate in your body; it is overeating and causing a major energy imbalance rule over your body.

Keeping your body's balance, coupled with focusing on high quality, wholegrain carbohydrate sources is one step closer to achieving better overall health.

> ♦ Avoid of sugar-sweetened beverages soda, energy drinks, and fruit juices. AVOID DRINKING YOUR CALORIES!
> ♦ Focus on wholegrain and whole foods.
> ♦ Consume five to seven servings a day of vegetables and two to three servings of fruit per day.

OMG! Fats!

Now, here's a family of macronutrients that are really misunderstood. Dietary fats are divided into saturated, unsaturated (monounsaturated and polyunsaturated) and *trans*-fat. This family of macronutrients can be animal-based and plant-based. A simple way to distinguish between saturated and unsaturated fats is by looking at their shape. This means that due to their differing chemical structures, saturated fats and *trans*-fat tend to be more solid at room temperature (such as butter), while their unsaturated counterparts remain liquid (vegetable oil).

Regardless of what kind of fat you're consuming, every gram of the above family of macronutrients will provide you with 9 calories per gram. However, you should be aware that fats differ in quality, and as I have mentioned earlier, your choices will dictate your future body shape and health. Healthy fats such as Omega-3 fatty acids; a special kind of unsaturated fatty acids will help you remain healthy.

I cannot stress the importance of consuming moderate quantities of unsaturated fats as they are crucial for your body to absorb fat-soluble vitamins (A, D, E and K). This group of vitamins is crucial for your vision, bone health, immunity, and blood coagulation, and as their name indicates, they can only be absorbed by the body using fat as opposed to the rest of the vitamins family which are water-soluble (think vitamin C for instance). Hence it is important for you to have a balanced diet that includes all macronutrients in moderation.

In addition to assisting your body in absorbing fat-soluble vitamins, fats are essential to produce certain hormones, the insulation and protection of neurons, as well as the production of certain fatty acids that are essential for our bodies.

Reminder: in nutrition, the term essential means that the macronutrient in question cannot be produced by the body and needs to be included in the diet.

Unsaturated fats play a major role in upholding our health. This might sound a little bit counter-intuitive, but they assist the body in lowering/regulating LDL cholesterol (low-density lipoprotein) levels, also known as "bad cholesterol," and increase HDL Cholesterol (high-density lipoprotein) levels, which lower the risk of heart disease. This is how crucial good fats are for your overall health!

> *But fat will transform into fat when consumed,*
> *isn't that right? What happens when I eat fat?*

This is in fact a very popular myth, as I mentioned previously, fatty acids are crucial for your body's functions and are assigned a long list of vital chores. Only in excess will they be transformed into adipose tissue. This means that once you start consuming more than you expend that fat will start building up.

Eat in moderation and eat mindfully, listen to your body, it knows what it needs.

To answer the second part of your question, good fats (including bad ones) will help you taste the food longer. The way fats coat your mouth is known to distribute flavors to more taste buds making your mouth "happy."

The second thing I'd like to mention is the fact that fats require a lot of energy to break down into their simpler forms. This means that consuming a balanced diet that includes an adequate quantity of fats will help your body burn calories more efficiently. Yet, this will be optimally performed when coupled with a healthy lifestyle and good bouts of exercise.

What about trans-fat and saturated fat?

These are "bad" fats you should avoid. Saturated fats are usually found in animal-based products, palm oil, etc. and are of no nutritional value. Humans are required to consume healthy fats, such as Omega-3 fatty acids, which are a special kind of unsaturated fatty acid. So, if you are a fish and/or nuts lover, you'd be ecstatic to know that they are packed with heart-healthy fats.

- ◆ Use liquid vegetable oils (such as canola oil, which is the most nutritious vegetable oil as it contains omega-3 and omega-6 fatty acids, vitamins E and K, and 7 percent of unsaturated fats.)
- ◆ Avoid overly heating plant-based fats as they can easily switch from unsaturated to saturated and trans-fats.
- ◆ Include fat-free or low-fat milk/dairy products in your diet.
- ◆ Use oil-based salad dressing and couple it with lemon or lime.

> ♦ Consume lean cut meats, chicken breast and other non-fatty meats.
>
> ♦ Low-fat plain yogurt is a great substitute for sour cream.
>
> ♦ In short, avoid saturated and trans-fats at all costs as they increase the risk of developing arterial plaque and heart disease.

Vita-mania and the Supplement Craze

When it comes to vitamins and other supplements human beings are going through a craze. We look at the boxes and packages of products claiming to give us the body and mind that we want, again falling into the same trap as in the case of fad diets. The funny part is that much of these vitamins and supplements go in and out of fashion before you could even be taking them long enough to see any effects. You'd suddenly hear your neighbor talking about some new pill that he's taken and how it had made him stronger, more virile, and happier or just helped him lose weight.

Grab any supplement and read its benefits. Be mindful of the way the sentence is structured. What do you see?

The most flagrant thing you see on these products is that they *may* help with whatever they are supposed to be doing. This means that this supplement which is supposed to help you lose fat – and I am talking about fat burners as a first example – only *may* do so, and here comes the disclaimer, given that it is coupled with a proper diet and exercise regimens.

This also applies to various vitamin supplements that have very appealing claims to the uneducated eye and ear. There are many great supplements that will help you with your gym performance and with your overall daily tasks, but do not get engrossed in the overpromises that salesmen make when they offer you samples. A lot of what you see out there is the product of monitoring closely how customer behaviors change and how to create new needs.

I advise you to head over to your physician, run a few tests, and just like diets, you will select the supplement that best suits your body's needs (given that you require the use of supplements at all).

Taking supplements might not always have immediate adverse effects, and if you Google your way through what works and what does not, you will notice that you rarely get any clear and definite answer regarding the consumptions of these innumerable tablets. Water soluble vitamins might be considered relatively safe, given than they are filtered out by your body; however, fat-soluble ones stick to the body since they are not flushed out via the kidney through water, and are usually accompanied by dangerous toxicity.

When you think of fat-soluble vitamins, you rarely consider the fact that they can be quite poisonous when taken in large amounts. Now, thankfully, large amounts are not found out there in nature. Yet, with the production of synthetic vitamins, hypervitaminosis A, D, E and K can be easily reached. It is crucial for you to know and for me to shed light on a detail that is mostly overlooked, and that is the difference between isolated vitamins and antioxidants, as opposed to naturally occurring ones. What I mean to say is that when you consume fresh, natural ingredients, vitamins, minerals, and nutrients come into your body as a network sharing electrons and balancing each other out. However, when you consume tablets thinking that you are providing your body with the recipe for miraculous health, the cons outweigh the pros, since isolated vitamins and antioxidants become free radicals.

Free radicals are chemical compounds that have an unpaired electron (a subatomic particle with a negative charge), making them highly reactive and unstable. In other words, the natural balance of their atomic structure has been lost. Simply put, such chemicals will not have any positive impact on your body, but rather have a wide spectrum of negative repercussions, starting with impaired vision, as is the case with hypervitaminosis A, which is akin to deficiency in said vitamin. Another negative effect of hypervitaminosis A is skin irritation and bone pain. I have created a table showing some of the most common toxic effects of hypervitaminosis A, D, E, K, along with simplified explanations of why such things might occur.

	Function	Deficiency	Toxicity	Sources
A	Sustains eyesight, necessary for healing wounds, necessary for growth and supports immune functions.	Low night vision, dry eyes, low immune system, skin irritation.	Headache, vertigo, bone pain, nausea and vomiting, hypercalcemia, hyperpigmentation, and skin irritation.	Dark green and deep yellow vegetables, egg yolk, liver, breast milk and its synthetic powder formula for infants.
D	Bone formation, calcium, and phosphorus absorption in the intestine.	Rickets (bowed legs, cranial bossing, etc.)	Hypercalcemia (very high blood calcium levels), vomiting and nephrocalcinosis (too much calcium deposited in the kidneys)	Sunlight as it activates the 7 dehydrocholesterol in the skin, egg yolk, liver, infant formula.
E	Antioxidant in tissues, coenzyme, and neuromuscular function.	Hemolytic anemia in the case of premature and newborn babies, degeneration of the retina, diminished response to tapping or hyporeflexia, spinal cord and cerebellum degeneration; spinocerebellar degeneration	Interference with vitamin K functions, slowing the clotting, hence adding to bleeding time. It also suppresses blood's reaction to iron.	Infant formula, breast milk, liver, egg yolk, leafy vegetables, wholegrain breads, wheat germ.

	Function	Deficiency	Toxicity	Sources
K	Blood clotting and synthesis of intestinal bacteria.	Prolonged blood clotting, hemorrhagic manifestations in newborns.	Might cause hemolytic anemia and jaundice.	Vegetable oils, green leafy vegetables, pork, and liver.

Table 1.1: The effects of deficiency and toxicity of vitamins A, D, E and K.

Vitamins in their naturally occurring states are not poisonous. If you look at the table above, you will notice that most of the mentioned vitamins are found in the same foods. This means that they come in complexes, as opposed to what is marketed these days in pills as isolated vitamins and antioxidants. Once you start altering the natural balance, there will be repercussions. We are not supposed to nourish our bodies with tablets and pills, (unless there is grave deficiency of course and following your physician's instructions) but our purpose is to find everything out there in natural, fresh ingredients. Historically speaking, many deficiencies, such as the famous vitamin C deficiency in sailors – scurvy – which was lethal and affected body and mind, were cured by providing sailors with citrus fruits during their travels. Another historically known fact is that countries with short sunny seasons have had their share of vitamin D deficiency, which had caused impaired growth in children and caused rickets; a case which left children with soft bones and bowed legs to say the least. The solution to this predicament was in cod liver oil;

a foul, fish smelling oil that was administered to children at a young age to avoid vitamin D deficiency.

The importance of consuming fresh ingredients and their impact on the overall physical and mental health cannot be negated. It is in the natural complexes and compounds that you will find healing.

The Human Microbiome

I have already mentioned how food can refresh the human microbiota. This part is part and parcel of what maintains physical and mental wellbeing. Our bodies contain a staggering 100 trillion microorganisms that literally outnumber our cells. Our microbiomes weigh about 200g and are present in the gut. I know that thinking of having microbes in your body seems like a strange thing, but not all microbes cause us to be sick or in other terms pathogenic; in fact, the ones that we have in our bodies, and that are influenced by our food and liquid intake help us digest our food, regulate the immune system, assist our bodies in fighting infections and produce vitamins B, B12, thiamine, riboflavin and vitamin K.

Another vital piece of information is the gut bacteria's impact on our mental health. It is so important to the extent of being called our second brain. This collection of organisms has a mind of its own and we use it all the time. Its impact on our overall health, including our mental one cannot go unnoticed. Any imbalance affecting this major player will have several repercussions on our emotions, thought processes, hence our actual brain; this is the gut-brain connection.

Gut bacteria are called the Enteric Nervous System, which means that it has to do with our intestines and has been proven to influence our judgment. These microbes are not invaders; they are there to make us feel better. However, when things go out of balance, many ailments tend to strike the body, ranging from weight gain to depression.

Muscular dystrophy, multiple sclerosis, the accumulation of microbes over time, the altering of metabolic processes and abnormal immune responses, such as autoimmune diseases are some of the most recurrent illnesses. Imagine the power of the microbiome; it can turn the body on itself.

To keep your second brain a happy one, I have compiled ten tips that are easily achievable:

> ◆ Increase fiber intake to around 30 to 40g per day. Despite it being double the recommended intake, fiber has innumerable benefits ranging from reducing the absorption of fat and sugars, preventing heart ailments and cancer.
>
> ◆ Increase your intake of seasonal fruits and vegetables, which goes in line with point number one, but add to that the uptick of macro and micronutrient ingestion.

- Eat nuts, seeds and berries, and moderately drink coffee and green tea. These foods and drinks are rich in polyphenols, which are a form of antioxidants that energize microbes.

- Eat fermented foods, such as unsweetened yogurt, raw milk cheese, cabbage, and chili, as well as soybeans.

- Stay away from aspartame, sucralose, and saccharine since they tend to reduce gut diversity, leading to obesity and diabetes.

- Avoid processed foods saturated with sugar, trans fat and other chemicals such as emulsifiers as they upset your gut.

- Avoid antibiotics in case you do not really need them (ask your physician) and steer clear of non-essential medicines such as paracetamol and antacids.

- Avoid overusing antibacterial sprays, hand gels and any such products as they may impact your gut bacteria.

- Avoid supplements as they are processed foods that can reduce microbe diversity. Focus on enjoying real fresh foods as sources of nutrients.

> ♦ Go on a hike, adopt a dog too or any other pet of your choice; studies have shown that rural areas can have a direct impact on our guts, as well as living with pets

Ups & Downs, Breakthroughs and Discovery

It is super easy to let go, and binge eat; however, being human and having the ability to understand our surroundings, as well as our internal processes, makes us accountable for mistreating our bodies. What I would like to shed light on, is the fact that mindful eating is not eating so little that you starve yourself, but to be in aware of the quantity and quality of food you are ingesting. This is easier said than done since our brains crave what is on the table until it is removed and hidden from sight.

Eating mindfully is an essential habit that you must learn, and I learned it the hard way. Allow me to explain. I had always had a flair for investing in startup companies and developing new businesses. I had a deep passion for this because it allowed me to share my skills and experiences with my peers, and I deeply cherished it. With two children at home, and business going so well, my wife and I felt that we were blessed. It wasn't until one little incident sent us into a whirlpool of stress and devastation; my wife was seven-months pregnant with our third child when she fell down the stairs in our newly built house. She remained dazed for hours and was oblivious to what had happened to her. With a broken cheekbone, and a broken arm, she was in a deep state of shock physically and mentally, but our child, thankfully, was still alive. However, the sedatives and narcotics that she was administered during her two surgeries, alongside the antibiotics had halted our baby's growth.

Our baby boy was born underweight, yet healthy, which allowed us to go back home a week following his birth. However, it wasn't before long that he contracted a respiratory infection called Respiratory Syncytial Virus (RSV); an infection that targets premature babies. Our child went into a coma as his lungs filled up with mucus. He had to be hospitalized for weeks in an intensive care unit, be administered immunity-suppressing medication, which gave other infections leeway to wreak havoc on his frail little body. The following year could only be described as a poisonous, a vicious cycle of fatigue and stress. I was trying to remain strong for our children, focus on saving our third child and manage my business, which at that time also has suffered greatly from my absence.

Now, here's the catch, that vicious cycle pushed me into an unhealthy lifestyle; I suffered from a mild heart attack and had to be hospitalized too. This was the turning point in my life; it was one of those breakthroughs that leave you shaking as reality and awareness intertwine right before your newly opened eyes. I was further dissociating myself from my mind and yet somehow, everything seemed to make sense. I took advantage of the strength and lucidity that I had discovered

51

through my will to save my family to go back to university, earn two master's degrees, an MBA in general management and another in business engineering and digital transformation. I focused my energy on establishing healthy habits, crafting a healthy lifestyle, researching integrative health, medicine, and ways to bolster good mental health.

Despite the massive amount of energy and the deep dedication that it required, I felt at peace. I was further building a future that fits my new vision. I become deeply interested in the health sector, my curiosity eventually leading me to becoming the CEO of a rehab center. It was another opportunity for me to learn about what works and what doesn't with individuals suffering from mental and physical ailments. Something deep inside further pushed me to dig deeper into healthcare. So, I traveled around the world visiting one rehab center after another, learned from the best and developed my own healing techniques. I researched many treatment methods and pushed my education further over the years. I learned psychology, nutrition, CBT, MBSR, NLP and more. I took numerous courses to be well versed in the management and transformation of organizations. I wanted people to find their way back to a life with purpose, meaning, good health and true happiness.

I cannot stress the importance of creating healthy habits, because making a difference is not practicing something only once or twice. Creating good habits is rather what you allow your mind to absorb and accept, hence shaping the present and future you. Since the human mind does not differentiate reality from illusion, and since we humans are usually house and life-trained, this means that we can retrain ourselves to see beyond what we have been taught. This means that with that most precious and fulfilling tool that we acquire during our years (especially during adulthood), and by that, I mean awareness; we can break our old habits. Instead of not listening to our bodies we can learn to replace such negative habits with ones based on respecting and properly feeding our bodies with only that which is of great value. Mind you, when I say, "feed your body," it applies to proper and healthy food, as well as proper and healthy thoughts.

To further prove this point, I feel the need to mention a major problem with the western diet; one that is of grave importance; *processed foods*. Much of what we consume as part of a relatively healthy diet is more or less processed. When food is processed, much of the fiber, many nutrients, and vitamins – mostly the vitamin B family – are destroyed, hence extending the product's shelf life, and softening the overall texture. This does not stop here, much of the food that we see sitting there for months on beautifully arranged shelves contain massive amounts of sugar and salt that act as preservatives, which takes us back to the importance of reducing the consumption of sugar and salt at all costs. The solution to this predicament would be to prepare your own food whenever you can; it's beneficial to learn cooking and baking skills, it only takes a few tries and you'll be fast on your way towards expertise. To add fuel to the fire, large companies that cater to the masses, use low-grade raw materials to increase their profit margins. And so, I wonder, is it really worth it? Ingesting such badly selected ingredients, building up toxins and suffering the consequences of having bad habits?

When I turned to healthy foods, I found that my thinking became clearer than before. Sure, I used to have enough energy, but my body kept on having this urge to consume more. I wondered why this persistent feeling could not be satisfied. I listened to my body, learned to understand the reasons behind the urges, I became the awareness behind the feeling. I observed what was going on the inside, only to find out that most of what was poking me and trying to grab my attention was, in fact, a bodily demand to respect higher needs. My very Being was calling out in distress, it felt... I felt empty.

The nutritional value of what we are eating has become so low that many foods are these days described as empty calories. From Soda to candy and other attractive products, our bodies are solely recharging in energy, minus the health benefits that truly give our organisms the appropriate boost.

Ever wondered why you are having mood swings? Have you ever considered the fact that the lack of certain nutrients, vitamins and minerals has detrimental effects on our mental health?

I would like to establish a comparison between a bag of sweets and a bag of spinach. The first is simply an energy-packed product that is devoid of any nutritional value. You will most certainly gain weight should you consume this while counting your calories, if that is what you were wondering, because of the stress that deficiencies put on your body. The second option might not sound as attractive, but it is surely nutrient packed.

Tip: It is better to eat spinach with vitamin C-rich foods such as tomatoes and lemon juice, or with heme-iron-rich foods, such as lean meat, to increase non-heme iron absorption.

I have undertaken a journey from being a typical twenty-first century individual who is just a consumer to a healthy Being focusing on body and mind health. My research has led me to unveil so many facts regarding our modern diets. For instance, in the past sixty years, our consumption of sugar has dramatically increased due to the introduction of canned and processed food. This has pushed me to purchase ingredients from fresh markets, and what an impact that has had on my well-being and on my family!

We have started avoiding pseudo-healthy foods that are fortified in vitamins and minerals, opted for homemade whole foods, and in short, we created colorful dishes out of seasonally available ingredients. I have transformed food selection and preparation into an experience for my family. I have made of food something that is fun to prepare – regardless of whether it is time-consuming or not – and to serve. The way my family and I have altered our lifestyle made us proud of our homemade dishes; we had gone back to food that nourishes the body and provides it with enough clean power to reach its higher self. We have become an even more tightly-knit group thanks to cooking our meals together. Involving the whole family was surefire way to get things going the right way and to make it more of an enjoyable pastime rather than a chore.

Tip: Dedicate a couple of days throughout the week to preparing your meals and freezing them. This will allow you to save time and preserve some homemade goodness for when you are super busy.

You have the power to transform that which looks quite complex, probably messy, and boring too, to something that is totally and intrinsically enjoyable. There are a few things that I will be repeating over and over; one of them is that you control your reality, the way you regard everything around you, the way you perceive your feelings. These three points will dictate your life path. I, therefore, call on to you to consider the following:

- ◆ All that is easy and quick will come at a price, most notably at the expense of your own health.
- ◆ Take a stepwise approach, meaning that baby steps are more applicable and more sustainable

than trying to change the world/your life in one
go (you can't change the world, it's not your job).

♦ Make sure to know what really requires your
attention the most. All changes that can wait will
have to wait. And so, give priority to what is
crucial for your wellbeing. Set a change list.

Tip: One way to make yourself accountable, and maybe a
way to formalize this whole healthy agreement, is to sign a
contract with yourself. This contract should look legitimate
and should include your objectives and a set timeframe. You
will be then triggering a psychological change in your life and
setting yourself on the right path with the right mindset; a
mindful mindset, which will lead you to fulfilling that contract.
Talk about healthy gratification!

Fad Diets

Just like everything else nowadays, trends have found their
way into the food industry. Year after year, we notice how
celebrities trumpet how they lost weight thanks to some diet
with a strange, yet attractive, name. Regardless of who is
marketing these claims and given the large amount of cash that
rains on whoever backs such fad diets, science is the only truth
that I seek to share here.

There is a big difference between fasting and starvation.
Whenever you are fasting, you will have to fulfill all your

body's requirements no matter what, otherwise you would be going head on into starvation. What I mean is that you will have to refill on all your calories *AND* nutrients at a later stage. You, therefore, cannot cut down on carbohydrates, proteins, fats, or any other nutrient to survive on an insignificant number of calories. Respect your body and constantly listen to it. Less does not mean more in this case. Less means *WAY* less for your body, which will push it to store fat and to break down your muscles for energy. Your body will lose water weight and your metabolism will slow down to a screeching halt because of the lack of calories and nutrients. Remember, just like fire requires wood, your body requires food to burn fat reserves. Be careful of fad diets that can lead you to hitting the wall or to plateau while attempting to shed weight the wrong way. Any restrictive diet, which forbids you from consuming certain food groups, will surely help you lose weight. However, your body will crave those food groups again and once you go back to your regular eating routines, you will experience what we call a rebound, which is another way to tell you that you will regain the lost weight due to binge eating and a deteriorating rapport with the right food.

Fad diets follow us everywhere, from the internet to bookshelves. You will notice how publications dating back to 2016 and even earlier, will re-emerge thanks to some celebrity marketing such diets as being effective. But let us not forget that celebrities have the luxury of spending hours and days at the gym, whereas your average Joe might be able to afford access to a gym, but not to personal training and proper follow-up. Be skeptical and do not believe everything you read and hear about; research and professionals are your best friends in this case.

Going back to selecting the proper diet, I can only reiterate a previous idea that I have shared and that I truly believe in; one that focuses on individual needs. Many people run to dieticians asking for a quick fix only to be disappointed and discouraged. This is not the way to go! Simply put, such requests will only lead you to the path of chaotic consumption, misinformation and eventually weight gain.

What's best for you, works for you!

A businessperson's needs differ from those of a student, and still, under those two examples that I have just provided, there exists several subcategories with another set of specific needs and wants, which implies that no human being is akin to another. This, in turn, is another way of saying, the diet that works for you will or might not work for your friends, siblings or that stranger walking down the street.

Moreover, the diet that you will be selecting must at all costs be based on what you like most. You might be the type that likes a challenge and go for a diet that restricts a macro that you like, or an ingredient that you love. Such decisions will not lead you to a sustainable diet and lifestyle. Diets are not there to torture you, they are not some kind of abusive way to force your body into the shape that YOU want, that your MIND wants. I urge you to forget photoshopped pictures of celebrities that might not even be close to that shape in real life and choose the diet that will make the process a happy one.

Happiness means less cortisol (a stress hormone), which means less water retention and less fat deposits within your body. It's simply scientific and mathematical.

I have tried almost every diet program until I settled for intuitive and mindful eating. I eat everything from carbs to proteins and fats given that they are clean, unprocessed, and fresh. I also focus on not overeating or making food a way to deal with stress. I have become aware of what is causing these emotions and feelings and observing them. Keep in mind that you need to put your needs under the microscope, select the diet that makes you want to adopt it, and should you start questioning your decision, place both your feelings and the diet under the microscope and conduct and self-evaluation in an objective way. The Do's and Don'ts:

- ◆ Choose a diet you like and that fits your lifestyle.
- ◆ Caloric deficits should not exceed 500 calories.
- ◆ Diets that are too restrictive will only lead you to rebound.

- ◆ Consider your diet as a kind of relationship with your food, and show it love. Make it enjoyable!
- ◆ Always ask your physician or dietitian for advice.
- ◆ Food also affects your mental health, and the lack of nutrients is detrimental to your overall emotional, psychological, and physiological processes.

Your Fitness

Fitness is another facet that I have come to focus on for a few years now. After suffering from a mild heart attack, dealing my child's health problems and other stressors, my body was screaming at me asking for something to let this negative energy out. What better way to live healthily and happily other than through creating a fitness routine? Imagine, working out is like taking 11 medication pills in one go! Nobody would want to take eleven pills every day, so hit the gym or just go for jog, it's miraculous!

I would love to share with you the five components of fitness, the health benefits of proper exercise, one's own fitness recommendations, the impact of overload, FITT, the reversibility principle of exercise, health risks associated with performance-enhancing drugs and sports injuries and how to avoid them. While getting to know more about physical fitness, you will also see its link to mental health and how they work synergistically.

Physical fitness comprises five components, which are cardio-respiratory endurance (to train for a long period of time without feeling tired), muscular strength (the amount of force that one can produce in a single effort), muscular endurance (the ability to repeatedly exert force against resistance), flexibility (the joints' ability to move in a restriction-free and pain-free fashion) and body composition (is the percentage of fat, bone, water and muscle in the body). A well-balanced body is one that has all its antagonistic muscles equally strong and is in line with the five fitness components. When we talk in terms of improving cardio-respiratory endurance, we are specifically considering aerobic exercises, which allow your body to go through long and hard workouts without reaching breathlessness and fatigue. Examples of cardio-respiratory exercises include, but are not restricted to, walking, running, jogging, some kinds of dance and step training. The opposite of aerobic or cardio-respiratory exercises is anaerobic exercises. Anaerobic exercises develop a deficit in oxygen within the body that needs to be made-up later. Such exercises usually include workouts that last between ten seconds and two minutes, such as weightlifting and sprinting.

I have been to various gyms throughout my attempts to reach optimum health. If you look at me, you will notice that I am not your typical fitness/gym enthusiast. In fact, I have shed unhealthy weight and coupled my workouts with a healthy lifestyle while keeping the body that best works for me. I did not become buff, neither did I take steroids to cut corners or solely focus on the aesthetic part. I was exercising for the sake of keeping a good fitness level that allowed me to have a good response to routine.

Physical activity surely has a major impact on aesthetics; it usually brings about changes that are seen to the naked eye. Fitness goes beyond that, and physical activity is closer to therapy than anything else. Physical activity has a plethora of benefits in terms of providing your muscles with a way to grow, strengthening your bones, lowering cholesterol levels, lowering blood pressure, increasing your resting metabolic rate (meaning that you will burn more while at rest), utilizing fat stores for energy and flushing our toxins; his list is non-exhaustive.

Fitness is your free way towards mental health as well. I invite you to stand up and perform jumping jacks over a period of thirty seconds.

- ♦ If you have just eaten, please do not perform this test. Wait for a couple of hours then do it.
- ♦ Give it your all.
- ♦ Make sure you move your body in a coordinated way.
- ♦ Make sure you breathe properly throughout the exercise; expand your lungs!
- ♦ Enjoy those thirty seconds.
- ♦ Record how you felt afterwards.

How do you feel now?

From a scientific point of view, moving your body will immediately and positively affect your state of mind. It will boost your concentration and mood, and on the long run, exercising regularly will not only protect your body, but also your brain from burnout, depression, dementia, Alzheimer's disease, among others.

Right behind our foreheads resides the part of the brain called the prefrontal cortex that is responsible for decision-making, personality, attention, concentration and so on. Long-term effects of exercise on that specific part of the brain are a spike in concentration, a longer attention span and better memory formation. Yet, a small part of the brain is responsible for that, and it is located in our temporal lobes. The hippocampus is the hero of this transformation. Exercising will allow it to grow, and – SURPRISE! – create new brain cells! Yes! And this is directly linked to cardio-respiratory workout regimens which protect your brain from degeneration and allow you to store more memories. I will not ask you to spend hours at the gym, neither go to the gym at all. In fact, all you need is a little bit of space where you can perform moderate a thirty-minute exercise about four days a week. Moderate exercise is best defined as exerting enough effort to be able to sustain talk, but not being able to sing.

Exercise is the most powerful tool you have at your disposal, and it's for free!

Exercise has a transformative power. We were never meant to be sitting at desks, hunching over laptops and papers. Our bodies were created to escape predators, chase game, and climb trees and perform many other amazing feats throughout the day. In modern times, such activities have been transmuted into a different form of energy expenditure, exercise, and games. Moreover, our bodies can heal themselves very efficiently. In fact, they are perfect at doing so if provided with enough nutrients and proper exercise. Forget detox juices and all that nonsense!

Recent studies have dubbed sitting as the "new smoking". You might be skeptical as to whether such a comparison stands; however, it is scientifically proven. A large study conducted in Australia found that each additional hour of television watched per day translated to an 11% increase in mortality causes. Although this piece of information seems grim, this does not mean that it is impossible to fix. There are numerous ways to get your body moving such as having your smart watch remind you to move, using an exercise ball instead of a chair (it will help you develop stronger legs and better balance), you can even have a standing workstation. At the end of the day, what's good for you works for you. Look for the solution that feels right by listening to your body and understand its needs. I feel compelled to advise you not to over-train and overstrain your body! Doing so will only have negative effects on your overall physical and mental health.

What is overtraining? I have heard about it, but I couldn't really understand when I reach it. It's quite ambiguous!

In simple terms, overtraining is going overboard with training. It is divided into overreaching and actual overtraining or what is also called *staleness*. Overreaching is the first stage and is reversible. It is accompanied by unusual muscle soreness following many days of intensive training. The good news is that a few days rest will reverse the effects of overreaching. But, when it comes to staleness, your body would have sustained heavy damage from all the intense workouts you have been doing and it would take weeks, even months for your body to recover.

I advise to work out 4 times a week, i.e., Monday and Tuesday, rest on Wednesday, and resume on Thursday and Friday. Weekends can be dedicated to active recovery, which would mean that you could go for a nice slow walk, enjoy the weather, and move your body without counting calories burned. Active recovery is supposed to be a relaxing time. Remember to always enjoy the process.

Tip: If you ever feel that your performance is declining, do not take it as a sign that you need to train harder. You should take it as a warning sign and that your body is screaming and asking you to let it rest. Always be mindful of your body's signs as it clearly states what it needs.

I have always been an athletic person. Between the age of 14 and 22, I worked out almost every day as I was part of the Karate Swiss National Junior League Team. I had conditioned my body to undergo intense training and at that time, I had a great workout routine, which rendered me quite physically strong and accelerated my learning. However, as I started my own business, being part of the fitness world became somewhat a tedious endeavor. The healthy routine that I had established was lost. My mind was focusing on business, I was still young, my body was still full of energy; years of proper training had shaped me into a mean machine. And so, I was able to cope with the less healthy business lifestyle. I was also fortunate enough to be able to reincorporate physical activity into my life again later; I hired a personal trainer to oversee my training three to four times a week, I picked up tennis a couple of times a week and had a few other activities going on. My life was being revisited and reinvented with the power of physical activity; my calendar looked great with all my workouts sessions planned ahead!

Having intense workouts tailored to my needs was a way to justify my unhealthy eating habits. In other words, I was enjoying success, I was eating whatever I wanted, regardless of whether it was what my body really needed, I had no children yet, and I was living my life to the fullest as an any healthy, fit young individual would do. I set myself in a positive cycle that maintained my energy levels and overall wellbeing.

But what you sweep under the carpet will pop up later with the slightest change. With the advent of our first child – this was not a slight change, trust me on that! – My healthy routine crumbled to dust. It took me a while to adjust and rebalance myself as well as rebuild my routine. Having children is one of the most amazing and wonderfully rewarding things in the world. But kids are high maintenance Beings, and it can be challenging at times to understand why your child is still crying after gorging down a container's worth of milk, baby food and what not! If I could get a penny for every single time somebody asked me how I managed to keep a household, run a few businesses, and stay healthy, I would have surely become the richest man in the world. From day one, our first child - a beautiful baby girl - had colic's and struggled to digest her food. This situation went on for months, and my wife and I had difficulties sleeping, which was something we never had before. With the lack of sleep came under-recovery after my workout routines, which left me tired and sore.

Under-recovery or overusing your body is your worst enemy. Fast forwarding my story to the time following my third child's issues and my own heart attack, I delved deep into research. I tackled conventional medicine and visited physicians and specialists all over the country, which is known for having the best healthcare system in the world! Something was definitely going under the radar, and I wanted to expose it. I had so many questions that were haunting me. I wanted to understand what really put my son in this situation. I wanted to know why his immune system was so weak. Was this caused by my wife's accident while he was in the womb? Was it because of his premature birth? Was it because he was underweight? Or was it caused by all the above? Were there other causes that I was not aware of?

My research pointed me towards the more holistic approach. A healthy body will make your mind more resilient to stress, and a strong, resilient mind will, in turn, allow your body to be fully healed and in top shape. Visualize yourself as a cyclical entity. Look at your body and mind as providing each other with the energy to shift and adapt much like the members of a team. You can either have those team members play solo, which is not remotely the aim here, or operate as a tightly knit team. What is quite interesting is that the physical realm and the mental/emotional one is not so separate. In fact, the way you treat one of them will have direct and indirect repercussions on the other.

The first step to achieving wellbeing is to love your body. Love your body enough to let it move. Structure your day and incorporate achievable activities; these include simple workouts on your chair, talking around the office, standing, and stretching every now and then. Moreover, you can schedule your workouts and dedicate thirty to forty minutes of moderate physical exercise three to four times a week. Try to walk to the nearby grocery store and make that walk enjoyable, put your headphones on and just walk. If you have a meeting, make it a mobile meeting. Walking is a great way to tap into your problem-solving skills and an even better way to boost creativity. In fact, studies conducted by Stanford researchers have proven that walking and moving will open your mind to higher levels of thinking, and that participants in this study have discovered that their best ideas have come while simply walking. Using cold, hard science, other studies have exposed why such a simple activity caused an uptick in cognitive processes. The results came in and it was right under our noses; walking and any other cross-crawl movements – movements that use both sides of the body – force our brain's left and right hemisphere to communicate and coordinate. With neurons firing repeatedly and stronger connections being established between the two sides, our brains become more efficient and information exchange is rendered restriction-free. Such a development in the brain is not only one to boost our physical performance, but also trickles down to our thought processes and activities, such as reading, writing, learning in general and concentrating for long periods of time.

I am sure some of you are tech-savvy, so why not use any of the fitness gadgets out there, to estimate your caloric expenditure, count the number of steps you did and monitor your heart rate for optimal results? Look at physical activity as an adventure. Draw your path; start simple and build up your workouts to more intricate and challenging ones, and you will see results before you know it. Let me just explain the two systems that our bodies run on while working out: the aerobic and anaerobic systems.

A good example of an aerobic exercise is one that refers to exercise bouts that last longer than two minutes. It is described as a continuous state exercise and requires the use of oxygen to produce energy. The anaerobic system is divided into two: the adenosine triphosphate and phosphocreatine (ATP-PC) system, which provides immediate bursts of energy for exercises such as throws and sprints. The other anaerobic system is the lactic acid system, which provides enough energy for tough exercise bouts ranging between 10 and 120 seconds. This is usually accompanied by a burning sensation and the buildup of what we call lactate (a substance that our bodies' cells produce while burning food for energy) and metabolites inside the muscle.

A good way to exercise is to warm up for about 5 to 10 minutes performing dynamic stretches and movements at a slow pace and using half the usually required range of motion, followed by weightlifting with progressive overload (it means adding weights as you go) hence activating your anaerobic system, finishing with 10 to 15 minutes of bodyweight exercises that activate your aerobic system. Your cool down will be of 10 minutes of stretching and deep breathing as you lower your heart rate. Perform this sequence and you are guaranteed to lose water weight first, and then fat as you go.

Tip: Do High Intensity Interval Training or HIIT; give it your all ➔ 5 to 30 seconds of high-intensity exercise during your workout may help boost your metabolism.

As a woman, I am afraid to bulk up when I lift weights,
I love working out. But I don't want my shoulders to grow,
I want to stay feminine.

Here's one myth that always get me laughing because it touches two fundamental things: limiting beliefs and physiological myths. It is ironic how we can crave something and yet be so afraid to do it. Physical activity and athletes/fitness enthusiasts have always been subject to limiting beliefs. I mean to talk about the way they look, act and train. I cannot stress how disconcerting it is to see how society has shaped the way we look at the level of the masculine and the feminine. What makes a man or woman look good? This fear of looking other than what you are expected to look like is an illusion created by society and the shallow beauty norms set by various industries.

Would you rather have a frail and supposedly "feminine" body as opposed to a strong and physically able one? And NO! I don't mean having biceps the size of a watermelon, but a toned body with enough strength to do whatever *YOU* want.

You are not the image that society has built into your brain. You are the product of your self-care and self-love. When you start loving your body, loving your mind, accepting that you can shape yourself the way you see fit is the moment you will unlock physical and mental abilities that will shape your reality.

On the physiological level, a woman/girl, you will never bulk-up the way men do. Your body does not secrete enough testosterone to make you look manly. On the contrary, your limbs will become toned, your posture will become more upright and shining with confidence, your senses will become more acute, your brain will literally grow, and your reflexes will be enhanced.

There are numerous reasons why I advise to lift weights or workout with your body weight, rather than just rely on cardio. The first reason is that too much cardio will leave you burning muscle rather than fat. The misconception that accompanies weight loss is that it is a good sign. It is not always the case! What you see on the scale does not reflect what is actually happening inside your body; a drop in weight can actually be related to either fat loss or muscle loss. A good and cost-free way to know if you are doing well is by watching your shape at home and the way your clothes fit you. Trust your eyes!

You will be able to determine what you need to focus on in terms of exercise and nutrition, which are two side of one coin.

Just like nutrition, having seasonal exercises is a great way to stay entertained and motivated while working out. If you have the luxury of enjoying four seasons, plan your workouts based on your environment. Experience life and the seasons while shaping your body and mind, it will keep boredom at bay and make this healthy commitment a happy and long-lasting one.

Celebrate the sun! Make use of the long days to spend more time outdoors. Plan group activities, such as group cycling, hikes, football, and basketball games. Make summer your friendly competition season! Other nice activities include yoga, and swimming.

Simply Fall! Once the heat starts to dissipate and days grow a little shorter, you'd feel like you are ready for some introspection. Choose your favorite strength-building exercises and perform them in a circuit, back-to-back with as little rest as possible; think squats, deadlifts, rows, pushups, medicine-ball throw. Try to complete each circuit three times with 10 to 12 repetitions for each movement.

If you are looking for something with less grit, focus on your breathing with exercises such as sprinting, vinyasa yoga, hence enhancing your strength and mobility through breath, such exercises also include indoor cycling and bodyweight exercises.

Win Winter! Once the cold weather starts to take over, you would be quite tempted to sit with your cup of coffee or tea watching series and movies. Gamers and series junkies especially like this season as it is the perfect alibi to stay in; however, why not focus on flexibility, coordination, balance, and concentration? Go for ancient disciplines such as Yoga, Pilates, etc. make it a time to heal yourself inside out.

Low to moderate-intensity workouts are also an alternative during this period as they allow you to conserve your energy to fight off the cold and give your joints and muscles time to heal.

You can always go for snowy areas and enjoy the white vista while snowshoeing and skiing among other snow-related activities; these too are greatly beneficial if you want to maintain your endurance and strength.

Strong Spring! Life is coming back to nature, animals, birds, and insects are all buzzing with life, and so are you! Go out and after the cold winter's healing exercises, it is time to use that energy to reach new heights. Nature has designed us to perform at our best during spring; our hearts beat a little faster, our metabolisms spike and our mood changes to match the season. So, take your time and craft strength training workouts that match the sunny and moderate weather.

Go for more power, strength, and speed. You will notice how you will easily grow and reach higher fitness levels. Don't forget to rest and stretch! Stretching should be a part of your everyday workout as it will keep your body looking and feeling amazing.

Physical activity is an important part of our wellbeing. Without it our bodies will only degenerate. I have shared with you loads of stories regarding my journey and how increasing my fitness level has mentally and physically boosted me. Both I would like to stress the importance of dedicating at least thirty minutes a day to physical activity, regardless of what it is, to enjoy the spike of dopamine and to activate your brain's neuroplasticity. I invite you to love your body, take progress pictures, enjoy the process, and stay mindful of how you are growing stronger. The journey can be a little tough at times, but with the right mindset, you will always maintain optimal energy levels. Just remember, there is no final stop, only progress and beautiful transformations that await you! Trust your body! Trust your brain! Relinquish your mind and allow yourself to tap into the happiness that is rightfully yours.

Deep Sleep

I love sleeping. I have been in love with the ability to recharge my batteries and have focused intently on its importance following the birth of my children. Sleep is both our own superhero and superpower. It is only when we lay down in our beds and let slumber wash over us that we truly let our brains and bodies recover, reshape themselves, shed stress away and grow. However, I would like to point out that sleeping too little and too much have adverse effects on our bodies. Research has shown that sleeping for four hours in a day has the same effect as having 0.05% of alcohol in your bloodstream. Chronically sleeping for very long periods has further detrimental effects.

Sleep is a highly researched field with many prominent experts dedicating their lives to discovering its powers, and one of their most profound discoveries has been the relationship between sleep and routines. Just like any other routine, sleep can have positive and negative effects. So, I will not be recreating the wheel, rather just stating the obvious considering my own experiences and that of my patients.

Sleep is a major evolutionary feat of such a great importance that is the catalyst for learning, adapting, fighting diseases, such as Alzheimer's disease, and much more. For sleep to become a healthy routine, the average adult is required to sleep 7 to 8 hours daily. But here's the catch. The sleeping pattern that one must establish should be scheduled to start on a specific time – preferably before midnight – and spanning seven to eight hours. In other words, try to sleep and to wake up at the same time every day. I can already hear your objections in my head.

I have gatherings with friends from time to time, I have a party on the weekend, I can't just leave to go home and sleep so that I follow my sleep schedule to a tee.

I am not asking you to change your whole life, as most of the happenings around us are out of our control. Yet, the way we react to them is our responsibility; respecting your body is a sure path towards grow. If we are to look at the sleeping brain, we would notice that it is as active as when it is awake. Scientists have already shed light on the fact that sleep is not just about conserving energy and that what is happening inside the sleeping brain is vital to sustain our health and life in general. Babies for example sleep around sixteen hours a day, with waking periods ranging between one or two hours. This means that sleep plays a crucial role especially during the first few years of children's lives as they must learn so much.

With our need to learn and grow, sleep comes as a way to consolidate our knowledge and memories. How many times have you experienced memory blackouts after pulling an all-nighter? How many times obvious things seem to elude your brain? The names of people you are familiar with might suddenly need intense focus for you to remember.

I can tell you for sure that most of us have experienced such blackouts. The simple explanation for this is the obvious lack of sleep and the lack of memory consolidation. At this stage, I will have to mention the hippocampus, which is located deep within the brain and helps with encoding and storing memories. I also must mention the outer cortex, which is the larger outer layer responsible for creating associations between memories.

Studies conducted on babies have shown how sleep is crucial for the formation and retention of memories. Case in point, various experiments involving teaching toddlers a set of actions have shown that babies that napped right after learning three actions using hand puppets remembered them perfectly the next day, while those who did not nap, only fiddled with the hand puppet.

It might seem hard to believe that a good night's sleep might have a massive impact on memory consolidation, but it is a scientifically proven fact. If babies needed sleep to improve their long-term memory processing, adults also need it for a plethora of other cognitive processes. Sleep is a crucial step towards a healthy lifestyle and daily cognitive and physical performance.

We are learning at every moment of our lives. I am not talking in an academic way only, but in terms of living and doing simple things like filling a glass with water, switching the light on and off and so on. Our brain is always calculating how much time we need to get from the kitchen to the bedroom, how long a friend will take to reach our house. You are even now calculating how long it will take you to read this book and understand it. We are organic learning machines, and if man-made robots need to be switched off to cool down, then the human body needs its rest to become more efficient, smarter, and sharper.

I have struggled with shallow slumber even to no sleep at all following the various incidents that I have recounted earlier. I had become easily irritable, especially when it came to managing my own business. I could not bear the idea that something did not meet my expectations. I went into a vicious cycle of anger, repressing that anger, bottling up, exploding, and living in anxiety.

Later, I came across this saying:

> *"If you are depressed you are living in the past.*
> *If you are anxious you are living in the future.*
> *If you are at peace you are living in the present."*
> *Lao Tzu*

The words shook me to the core, it felt so spot on that my mind felt attacked and receded into the darkness. Those words were so obvious and simple, yet so powerful that I felt like I was overburdening myself and my whole existence with all that I could not control. I decided to alter my sleeping habits alongside everything else in my life. I developed a routine that involved taking a warm bath or shower, listening to binaural beats, calming music, affirmations and practicing meditation before going to bed. I even started avoiding series, as well as work that kept me awake all night. Stretching in the morning upon waking up to activate the energy flow throughout my body was one major habit and breathing exercises allowed me to loosen up any mental and physical tension, which kept me living in the present moment. The effects were and still are amazing; I can focus for longer periods of time and retain information much easier than before. Physical activity also helped me sleep better and deeper, which created another nice cycle of energy expenditure, recovery and memory consolidation thanks to my recovered fitness level and the healthy/optimized sleeping routine.

If we are to look at our brains as a household; daytime/conscious activity is when the hustle and bustle takes place. Everything is moving and a whole spectrum of cognitive processes is whirling around. Come the night, housekeeping takes places and what we thought was a simple lack of consciousness turned out to be even more complex than its daytime counterpart. Once you set your head on your pillow and drift into sleep and a cascade of gradually deep events take place. These events or processes collaborate much like team of specialists to give you all the benefits of sleep. I have mentioned memory formation and consolidation; however, sleep is also beneficial for our immunity. I had always wondered what in the name of all the energy in the universe happened to me. Conventional medicine treated my symptoms, but no clear answer was given to me as to what was triggering all those negative reactions; I was craving unhealthy calorie-dense foods, I gained weight, I never felt full, experienced back and shoulder pain, headaches were constant companions, neck pain kept me on edge. My connection with my body was severed and as I started to understand that it was not about just treating the organ and the symptoms, but my body in a holistic way that I saw deep sleep as the first and foremost remedy to my ailments.

So, as I started sleeping better, the simple act of breathing became easier, my immune system had the power to fend off sickness; my brain was able to remove its own waste as I rested during the night. It is quite interesting to know that our brains have their own waste removal system. Research has shown that the lymphatic vessels act as a drain that cleans this complex organ, hence preventing dementia and Alzheimer's disease.

Our bodies have an internal clock which works with our endocrine system to release hormones that signal time for bed. One such hormone is melatonin, dubbed the sleeping hormone, which is secreted by our pineal gland. Even though it is usually secreted by our bodies, blue light from smartphones, tablets, and other gadgets with screens can block the production of this chemical, which might keep you up at night, or at least hinder you from reaching and enjoying deep sleep. If you cannot avoid that blue light, try blocking it with eyeglasses or using the now built-in function in smartphones and tablets that alters the screen's frequency. You'll notice colors becoming a little warmer as you switch that function on.

In case your phone doesn't have such functionality, various free apps provide that same effect for free.

Sleep is part of your body's innate ritual to go into recovery and cleaning mode. Yet, it is crucial for you to not only prepare your temple, but also your room, which will house and protect your temple from outside interference. Below are obvious but mostly overlooked tips to create the optimal sleeping environment:

- Make your room a place for sleeping and your intimate relations. Keep work outside!
- Keep it dark and quiet
- Keep it cool between 16 and 22 degrees to allow your body to go into sleep mode.

Once you wake up the next day, step into the sunlight and let it wash over you. We tend to take sunlight for granted. But the simple act of standing in the sunlight upon waking reinforces your natural circadian rhythm to be awake during daytime and asleep during the night. Repeat that same step over and over during the day, absorb those healthy rays and keep your body's energy flowing.

Coffee is obviously loaded with caffeine and found in a variety of other sources, such as diet sodas, chocolate, a few medications, tea, and energy drinks. This stimulant – meaning that it makes us more alert – is considered healthy in moderate quantities. It is advisable to consume one to two cups of coffee before 10am to avoid remaining alert upon going to bed. Caffeine has a half-life of six hours; hence you are invited to manage your caffeine consumption according to your waking/sleep routine. What I am going to say next might be obvious to some, but will greatly impact on your sleep:

- ♦ Give your body a couple of hours to digest and absorb nutrients before going to bed.
- ♦ A cup of alcohol will take 1 hour to reach your bloodstream, so you better give it time before you hit the hay.
- ♦ Want deeper sleep for longer? Workout for 20 to 30 minutes a day but keep that activity to four hours before bedtime.

One last, but very important point I would like to mention is that with better sleep comes better hair, rejuvenated skin, better muscle growth and a more efficient metabolism thanks to a hormone that I have already mentioned: the growth hormone or GH. This particular potent chemical will be released into your blood stream if you allow your body to relax and rest properly. So, if you want to look your best and your youngest, give yourself the chance to wind down and enjoy the healing properties of GH.

The Art of Creating a Lifestyle

Just as amino acids are the building blocks of proteins, good rituals and habits are the building blocks of a healthy lifestyle. The bond that links all those habits is the selection of intrinsically enjoyable ingredients and activities. Most of what has been published out there has focused so much on the consumption of flavorless foods and exercise routines that leave you heaving and gagging; activities that do not sit well with our brains.

To create a habit, repetition and reinforcement called the habit loop is crucial. This is a three-step process that starts with a stimulus or trigger that tells your brain it is time to behave in such or such a way. The second step is the action itself that takes place, followed by the reward. The third step is positive reinforcement. This step is vital for embedding this routine into your daily life or in other words, transforming it into an automatic task.

Since habits are an intrinsic part of our human constitution and patterns of behavior, scientists were able to pinpoint the part of the brain responsible for habit creation: the basal ganglia, which is a set of structures connected to the thalamus at the base of your brain and is responsible for movement, pattern recognition, emotions, and memories. This means that this part of the brain has the power to associate all your functions under the umbrella of habit formation. What links rituals and habits to this part of the brain is the fact that they are patterns that we create either consciously or unconsciously; think behavioral psychology and the Pavlovian experiment but transmute it to a higher level of consciousness; choose the ritual and habit, and in this case the eating habit, that best suits you. Once you select the habit you like most, or the routine that fits your lifestyle, you will be able to reinforce it. This is feasible through rewarding yourself everything you make a small victory or slight progress. What is great about habits is that they become automatic hence allowing you to direct your concentration to entirely different tasks. Once you establish a routine and several rituals, you start giving leeway for your brain to enjoy the rest of what you do. Remember! A routine might be automatic, and a ritual can be repetitive, but it is always enjoyable and helps increase your dopamine levels.

Routines, Routines, Routines

Throughout my research and my attempts at understanding what makes human beings tick, I have come to the realization that a part of us does not see or perceive what is right there under our noses. Human beings are routine-based organisms that flourish once they find the adequate place to root themselves. Settling down and establishing routines is the first step that humans take whenever they move into a new place. This process helps them cope with change, understand their environment, and plan their routines accordingly.

I have come to know a man in his early thirties who has been living alone for the past six years. He had developed the habit of waking up in the morning at a specific time; at 8:15 am to be exact, preparing his coffee, having a healthy breakfast – this is another habit he had formed as part of his lifestyle – and reading while sipping his coffee. Some might look at this as a total waste of time.

I cannot disagree more; this routine helped this man prepare and warm up his brain for upcoming tasks.

You can be the type of people that just wake up and run around, fumbling through heaps of clothes, grabbing a granola bar, or anything edible right before hitting the road. You might be the opposite; a person who wakes up with the day's outfit already laid out, coffee machine needing only be switched on and breakfast ready in the fridge. You might even have another example for me that might add to my insight into the various types of morning people, but it will only serve to prove that we truly are beings of habit and routine.

With his coffee in hand, he – let's call him Ben – reads for an hour or so before facing the world. He puts his mind into a state of openness, warms up his neurons for the day ahead, and finally when he's done, turns on his laptop and tackles his tasks. Ben works from home. He has the luxury of managing his schedule. He was lucky enough to adapt gradually and slowly by establishing a specific set of routines that are crucial and specific to his person.

I do not like to read; I might even fall asleep.
What if I do not have a specific routine? What can I do?

A healthy routine does not come by easily. We usually tend to let ourselves be driven by impulses that change according to our lifestyle and sleep cycle. I have seen so many individuals go through so many changes every single day that it was confusing, even for me.

To craft your day in the best way, you must start small. And just like diets, you need to see what works for you. Routines and rituals are powerful tools will lead you to better planning and happier days. There is no way in this world that a person can go through their day without having some sort of conscious or subconscious routine. So, a good way to start is by looking back at your day and becoming aware of the simple things that we do and that make us feel good, while the absence of which might trigger some form of distress.

Have you ever reached school, university or work and suddenly realized that you had forgotten to do that one little thing that would make a whole difference to you? It might have been brushing your teeth, putting something in your bag, wearing your lucky sweater or simply drinking a glass of water, well, that is part of your routine and it got interrupted, regardless of whether it was important or not, that routine was unfulfilled, and you felt it. To some, it might feel as though it is something insignificant, to others, it might feel like their whole day went off course and their energy is off balance.

How can a routine be good to me?

Routines give our lives a certain meaning. There is to the life/routine relationship more than you would ever give it. Therefore, to understand how a routine can be of good use, one has to understand the roles they play for the good of our psyche.

Routines allow us to put our thoughts and decisions into action, which means that you will have a certain set of choices, from which you will be able to select what is good and let go of what does not. Having a finite set of choices allows us to remain anchored in the now, to remain stable. This, in turn, will provide us with leeway to face any upcoming changes with the power of adaptability.

But I am a creative person;
I can't restrict myself to a few choices.

When I say that you have a finite set of choices to choose from, this does not mean that you will be left with the feeling that you are sitting behind a desk, tied to a chair, and asked to work on the same things over and over again. Routines allow us to adapt to changes, become more resilient, and train our minds to find what works for us. This can be done creatively. Routine does not have to mean boring.

Establishing a healthy routine bolsters creativity as it allows our brains to forego the stress of daily activities, make room for problem solving and open the door for other positive faculties to take center stage.

Remember, you're not a robot! So, having a routine is not repeating the same action over and over again, it is more of a ritual that eases you into your day and comfortably preps you for what is to come. Being creative plays in your favor in this case, it allows you to choose whatever you have always wanted to do, and craft it into a routine. You might aim for a better fitness level, for better dance technique, better writing and so on, but the way you implement it is purely personal and an intimate endeavor.

To further delve into routines, all actions are patterns, and they tend to interfere and regulate the rhythm of our lives, so creating a routine is not only the best way to align your day, week, month, but most importantly organizing your eating habits. I have crafted my own breakfast routine, which is centered on preparing my own muesli. With the large quantities of sugar in the pre-packed ones, I have decided to rely on my intuition and scientific knowledge to buy my own fresh ingredients and mixing them in the morning. I cannot emphasize the importance of looking at the actual process of doing something and saying "well, this is fun!"

I regard the process of preparing my breakfast or any meal of the day as a pleasant activity. It is a very personal series of actions that will eventually lead you to a proper and healthier meal. This goes back to our relationship with food and how it all affects our brains. The way we handle food is very intimate. It is, therefore, quite important for you to understand that once you start giving it the respect and love it requires, you will make better choices.

It is more of an equation that joins:

(love × respect for your body) + (love × respect for food) = Life balance

When I say show love to food, it does not mean to go and binge eat what falls under the healthy tab, but rather develop the habit of preparing the food with love, it is the energy surrounding the action, the power that surrounds us all and that is what religions call a blessing; I call it intent.

Blessings are rituals, right? Why not include them for example in your food preparation. You will not have to do any special movements or recite any prayers or incantations. But you can set yourself in the mindset that this is a beautiful time to mix wonderful natural ingredients. This routine will then be interlinked with the fact that you are doing so because you love and respect your body. Listen to your body and choose fresh ingredients. Be mindful of your body's needs, for it is smart and does not require all those detox juices and fad diets; eat moderately and ENJOY the process!

Going back to routines, I would like to emphasize the importance of providing your body with enough energy in the morning through good, healthy eating routines. Listen to your body and provide it with whole carbs as a long-lasting source of energy, good proteins to rebuild itself, good fats for its usual functions. My relationship with food has changed over the years; it had started as a love-hate relationship, trying to read so many labels, trying to calculate my macros and thinking in terms of hormones and the impact that certain nutrients have on my body. This is no longer the case. It has become apparent to me now that the best diet is no diet at all. I want you to avoid all that food drama, yoyo-ing, turning your cheat day into a cheat week and steering clear of guilt by crafting the habit of success, the habit of proper food preparation that has your name signed all over it. I want you to have a sustainable lifestyle. Moderation and sustainability are key terms. Keep them in mind!

Routines help shape the day ahead. It is the decision to control what is controllable in your life and to cope with/accept what you cannot. Crafting a routine will make you the leader of your own life, as well as being practical and useful. This last word is the most crucial of all, since being useful is akin to that that causes ripples in the pond. Your routine(s) should allow you to feel powerful enough to create ripples and affect events and other people in the most positive way you can.

Routines are said to increase productivity and of a positive attitude. As I have mentioned earlier, routines will increase your dopamine levels, hence making you feel happier and physically well. I can describe good habits, routines, and rituals as the outline of a healthy personal and professional life. I cannot stress the importance of reinforcing the positive form of those ritual, habits, and routines, since their negative counterparts do have adverse reactions on quotidian life.

Okay! I am confused. Positive routines, negative routines.
Can you illustrate?

Let me clarify. Once you settle into a life of unproductive routine, you will fall into a vicious cycle. Take for example a senior that I had met years ago. Let's call him Bill! He drove around thirty kilometers every day to work, managed a team of electrical engineers, came back home, cooked whenever his wife craved one of his delicious dishes – he was an amazing chef! – he even ran his own restaurant. Bill was living an exemplary life. The secret behind his success and mostly the success of his own business; the restaurant, were his set routines. He was so organized that people sometimes just came to watch him clean his work surface, prepare the ingredients as he always did, knead the dough, bake burger buns, sit have his coffee and after saying a short prayer, tend to customers. Of course, he enjoyed the help of his girls, wife, and a single waiter. The routines I had just listed went in line with the ultimate aim of being alive. The ultimate purpose of life itself is to be productive, useful, and amassing positive karmic energy.

It is well known that people are like sponges, and our ability to internalize all kinds of information – be it in an active or passive fashion – does not really diminish. I am talking about our subconscious doing all the work. You might consciously think that passersby in a mall go unnoticed, their words, unheard, their actions unseen. You are terribly mistaken. Bill's story comes with so much more. Since he established his business, families grew fond of his little place. They gathered there, shared meals on regular basis and, thanks to Bill's calm/calming presence and welcoming attitude, individuals found themselves routinely taking their notebooks, and later laptops and tablets to work in a quiet corner, families gathered to have a nice homemade meal, a coffee and casually chat, while Bill's wife kept the place pristine. In short, they were a great team.

However, here comes what I like to call the fine print of life; Bill was let go of his job at the age of eighty-six. His restaurant was temporarily closed, and he had just bought a massive television set. The lack of productivity and of anything of significance to do around the house bought about anxiety, sadness, and later depression. He sat for hours on end watching the same wrestling matches repeatedly. This led to several health problems, among them irregular heartbeats, and a temporary cardiac arrest. Bill sank into a set of dark routines that did not involve watching television shows only, but also eating while doing so – a massive mistake anybody, old or young could do – and finally oversleeping.

Neuroplasticity: Exceptional Ability to Learn Faster

Neuroplasticity that's a mouthful, isn't it? If you're having trouble saying it, then practice it a few times. Neuroplasticity, or perhaps, the art of practicing, is often overlooked. The human brain is the most complex structure known to man; it can virtually store unlimited amounts of information, develop new pathways, and reorganize itself infinitely. That's where neuroplasticity comes in.

It is not by coincidence that I have tackled this topic right after stressing the importance of fitness and nutrition, for the former is a key component of our neuroplasticity. Your brain has the ability to reshape itself as a result of your interaction with your environment. This means that you are not born with already-set specifications; you can upgrade your brain without having to add anything to your already perfect constitution. The only requirements in this case are your very own experiences so as to give your brain the power of neuroplasticity.

Shaping your future self does not come at any expense. It is only the outcome of you living your life garnering all that new data. But you can make the process a more conscious one, which will add to its benefits and to your personal satisfaction. Any day-to-day tasks and routines are key to forming your future self. This means that once you decide to take up a new hobby, practice those piano scales, rehearse a choreography, or just sit down and write, your brain's neurons will start firing up, and the more you practice the more pathways are created. Any task will become more and more efficient and more enjoyable as you evolve. On the opposite end of the spectrum, not using a specific skill will only put those pathways to sleep, and then disregard them.

We can all rewire our brains based on our needs – emotions, physical or otherwise – hence shaping our path for the hours, days, even years ahead. Addiction for instance is quite interesting to look at from a neuroplasticity point of view. Drug abuse has been noted to majorly affect vulnerable people that seek gratification. The activation of the reward system in the brain is a double-edged sword, negative habits can be easily developed based on the thought of immediate happiness, satisfaction, and gratification. With repetitive drug-taking, the reward system is activated time and time again hence reinforcing the association between feeling good and the drug of choice, which also means reinforcing addiction. Cues will become more and more effective at reawakening the need for the used substance, leading to a seemingly unbreakable vicious cycle.

These changes and the way such habits become ingrained will later necessitate a deep understanding of brain pathways, their fundamental nature, and their causes. A holistic approach is required to allow medication, behavioral therapies, and nutritional corrections to be fully assimilated on the psychological and physiological levels. It is important to regard all kinds of addictions as neuroplasticity diseases, and to treat them as such. It is not the simple detoxification of the body that will heal the addict, but also the understanding of the cues and triggers that flare those dark needs. Addiction is usually linked to two types of neuroplasticity.

The first one is tolerance, and I bet you know how at some point your morning cup of coffee has become less-than-effective at giving you that buzz. Well, that is a change in tolerance, and it is related to addiction. In other words, the same dose of caffeine, drugs (medical or recreational) will not have the same effect with repeated use. The other aspect of this neuroplasticity disease is physical dependence and is namely seen in the form of withdrawal symptoms upon stopping abusing substances – think of that annoying headache upon missing out on your morning coffee, but only worse.

The latter form of neuroplasticity is usually seen in people that are required to take antidepressant, β-blockers, sedatives, and narcotics. These same effects have also been seen in individuals abusing substances such as alcohol, cocaine, benzos, and nicotine. It takes a very patient-specific approach to properly bring this vicious cycle into a halt. This means that solutions are adapted to the ways our patients have shaped their brains, and this is done through proper psychological diagnoses, psychiatric follow up, medical follow up and nutritional shifts towards healthier alternatives.

You might be a beginner, intermediate or even an expert in fitness and you might be reading this book for information or just a simple reminder of how straightforward, yet complex, our bodies are. Whatever your aim is, I feel the need to share with you the importance of alternative fitness.

What is alternative fitness?

Alternative fitness encompasses activities that do not fall into the traditional fitness definition or mode of exercise. There is a variety of activities that you can practice, which would make you sweat like you have never done before, while having the time of your life.

Pointe and pre-point ballet are a great leg work out! Imagine the strength you need, and the concentration required to stay perfectly still on those pointe shoes, or even on your demi-pointe. Ballet is a great way to develop a strong mind-muscle connection as you will be asked to focus on your overall posture, from your head to your toes. And no! Ballet is not only for girls/women, but there are also set exercises that are taught to both and others that are gender specific. Classical ballet is a great way into the dance world, and an even greater weapon against neuron degeneration. this genre develops your neuroplasticity thanks to its various movement combination that require much concentration.

Another fun alternative fitness class also related to dance is Hip Hop. If ballet endowed you with grace, this class would give you grit! You will dance to your favorite beats, break a sweat and shake off that stress while developing your strength, endurance, and memory. Hip Hop is fun and quite physically demanding, try it!

Aerial fitness is a beautiful discipline. Just like ballet, it will allow you to develop your flexibility and to trust your body. It is surely not for the faint of heart, but if you set your mind to it, you will eventually find yourself flying. This type of exercise is very much related to yoga in terms of movements, and is said to improve your strength, muscle definition and fat burning as you perform your exercises hanging in midair.

These are just three of the best alternative fitness ideas, but my aim here is to pinpoint the importance of alternative fitness in providing workouts that are multidirectional. Dance in all its genres, rock climbing and hiking, to name a few, will force you to move through all planes of movement, which will keep your heart and muscles alert to those constant change.

Your body's constant attempts to adapt to irregular movements will only force it to use more energy/calories.

MENTAL HEALTH

There have been many attempts at understanding the human mind, and with those trials, tests, and hypotheses there came revelations, more hypotheses and experiments that put the actual brain under the knife – at least hypothetically.

Mental health is having the ability and awareness to understand your own abilities and feelings; it is a state of wellbeing that allows you to cope with everyday stress, be productive and, most importantly, be useful. Productivity and usefulness are my favorite terms and here is why. A productive person is a happy person, but to reach optimal productivity, you must go through and overcome several feats. We all have the power to do so, yet somehow, we decide to forego our prerogatives and live-in stress, hence distancing ourselves from being who we really are and from reaching our potential.

How many times do we see ourselves get defensive and retract into the mind's embrace? How many times do we let our mood dictate the way we deal with the people around us? These defense mechanisms that we take as part of ourselves can only protect us so much. We either must "kill" the mind, face our fears and the consequences of our actions, or just live a life swinging between the past and future, letting the mind act as in ways it feels suitable while we suffer. We all want to live in the light with constant prosperity and peace. Yet, I can tell you that without journeying into the depths of Hades; the subconscious, without experiencing what it feels like to be in winter, without undergoing a cycle of life and death, there would be no resurrection and no spring.

I refuse The Autopilot Mode

Something I love about humans is their ability to choose. We are equipped with the best tool in the whole universe, which is our brain. We choose to ignore a ringing phone or an email from an annoying colleague (who might not even be annoying but must do their job). We decide to watch a movie, stop that movie, resume it, play a song, and ignore a notification on our smartphones and so on. Yet, sometimes we fall prey to involuntary actions that are nothing but automatic reactions.

We always tend to let our autopilot mode take center stage in our lives. We read without paying attention, and much of the time we let our mind blind our eyes to the text, so we must re-read a paragraph of two. We sometimes reach home without remembering how we drove all the way; we throw our keys somewhere as we enter our homes and later blame the whole universe for losing them.

Our brains are wired to automate much of what we do. It is a kind of efficiency-oriented, built-in option. The human brain wants to make everything easier and faster, so it rewires itself, creates pathways that bypass consciousness. We drive automatically, sing automatically, talk automatically, and forget automatically. Rewiring our brains with healthy routines is great, as it allows us to focus on other tasks and give them the attention they deserve. It is efficient to have new pathways liaise parts of the brain that were not so well connected and strengthen others that need to be strengthened, but why not train our brain to be mindful of what it is doing? Why not expand its capacity? You might be thinking that this is getting complicated, but I need you to focus your attention on several things that will make your life experience a more beautiful one.

Talking about mindfulness means to point you in the direction of being aware of what you are doing at a particular time, in a particular setting. This happens when you do away with your mind's chatter and enjoy the quietude of your mindful being. You don't have to do everything consciously, otherwise you would tire your brain, but what if you ate more slowly, enjoyed the texture and flavor of your food? Didn't that make you drool a bit? If it did, then congratulations! You have stepped into the mindfulness circle. It is important to teach ourselves how to be mindful of the times our brain tend or need to go into autopilot mode.

In order to do so, perform a "body scan"; focus on every part of your body, looking for tension and consciously relaxing your muscles, soften your facial muscles, take a few deep and slow breaths focusing on the air moving in and out of your lungs. Another thing that we overlook is the excessive use of smartphones. Once you get that little devil out of your hand, you will notice that at first you will undergo a soft of withdrawal symptoms; fear of missing out, hearing your phone ring when it's not, thinking that the screen is blinking when it's not. Then you will start noticing things in the real world. You will become more and more conscious of your body's movement, the trees or road outside your window, the sunlight, the rain, etc.

Another step you can take to be aware of autopilot mode is to go back to your passions and hobbies, such as sketching, coloring, building things. These are just some of the ways you can start cultivating awareness, mindfulness and most importantly control over the mind and the brain.

Your Mind: The Useful Thinking Tool

I have been out and about experiencing life and focusing enriching every moment. Throughout the years that I have spent building my businesses, building a family and a home for my family, I have seen myself fall so many times for what my mind told me was true. It was like I was fashioned in such a way as to believe whatever my eyes saw, and ears heard. My environment, society and even the whole presence of human Beings on this earth has established a set of rules to distinguish what is beautiful from what is ugly, to judge each other and to make keep our brains stuck in a loop. There have been many books on this topic, and I have experienced what it means to face the power of all the rules and regulations set by society. As you already know, I am of a Muslim background, my wife is Christian, and you might think that moving to Switzerland as a child might have provided me with leeway to live a judgment-free life; however, my union with my Christian better half has faced many obstacle's from a variety of sources.

We are superbly wonderful creatures. We have evolved on this planet to make the best out of it. Yet, with evolution came the need to set limitations as we feared most of us would wield the power within in a bad way. We are in dire need of a transformation; one that leads us away from what we have put ourselves in. We are in need of a wake-up call to that recalibrate our eyes to the truth that we are missing.

What we seek is right under our noses, yet with fear gripping us and forcing us to go through the past, searching for meaning and understanding, while at the same time projecting our expectations, fears and hopes into the future, we have fallen from grace; that was our fall from Eden, the fall from the bliss that enveloped our unadulterated Beings.

We are creatures that are in love with profound transformations, but the process scares us to the core. Any change can be scary, be it a new job, a new house, leaving one's own homeland or just buying a new shirt, we think and overthink trivial details.

When I say all things that we go through are mental, I profoundly mean it, and the need for transformation is one that is related to enlightenment. Many great authors have written about this, and I cannot but reiterate their words and echo the power that every printed utterance carries. I have mentioned the term Being on purpose instead of the mind; Eckhart Tolle made superbly good use of that distinction and has pointed out how we can reach enlightenment. He even defined it using Buddha's words as "the end of all suffering".

That definition is perfect in every sense and is nothing close to our mundane nonsensical view of what this process is. When we reach enlightenment, we tap into God inside us or what you might call the kingdom within. We were born with ability to shift reality and spacetime. It is not by coincidence that we are made of the same components as the universe. It is not by coincidence that we bear in our crania the most complex organ known to man, and probably the universe. We are beings of frequencies; we emit frequencies with our thoughts, receive and feel them. Even our eyes are frequency receptors and emitters as colors are visible frequencies. We are made of energy and energy is frequency and frequency become a conscious force through us. This is how we transform our lives.

A beautiful and powerful truth surrounds us, but our minds have confined God within in a tiny room. Mind you! We are not powerless, yet we surrender to the fallen angel – our mind - that we can easily overpower. Imagine that! God surrendering to the fallen angel! How paradoxical!

Why would we ever surrender to a fallen angel?
And why this specific description of what is controlling us?

Humans have always loved fallen heroes; humans have always loved fallen evil characters. Humans love a good sob story and with the power of storytelling. Our being is trapped within and forced to kneel before an inferior being conjured up because we love storytelling, we love illusions, and we love ascribing signs and symbols to things. We love inflating things and deflating others. We overthink what is simple and sometimes dumb down what is not as such.

This routine of giving leeway to our minds has established an unhealthy habit. This has led the billions living on this beautiful earth to consider their minds as infallible. This is not a call to kill your mind and sit in ignorance, on the contrary! Since we like giving roles and labels, why not give our minds a specific label and a productive/useful one that serves our Beings. Let's label our minds as the "Useful Thinking Tool". Nothing more!

With this new definition, you can actually view your mind as something that you can use on demand. Consider it as a tablet that with a specific set of uses, mostly ones that are related to daily tasks. You would then be able to close the lid, or lock that screen, hence halting any unwanted interference. So instead of having the mind control you, you would be controlling your mind, which is something most spiritual teachings have mentioned and preached for eons.

Beware! The mind is a trickster; it is a shape shifter, an illusionist, and what better way to enslave a being than by having it look at illusions. Sadly, despite having a divine part living within us, our brains remain limited by the mind and by the mirages that we are given. This faulty imagery has been created by the mind to keep us under check. Humans have siphoned off ancient knowledge and have turned us against ourselves.

The power I am talking about is not something occult and scary. In fact, it is really you on the inside, the pure canvas that you were upon leaving your mother's womb. It is a beautiful thing to try and feel (as opposed to understanding) how we were so pure and non-judgmental. You can reach that stage once again! You *will* reach that stage! The universe did not give us the power of thought and the power of awareness for the sake of weaponizing us against each other. On the contrary, the power of thought and the power of the word itself, coupled with awareness, make up a divine and positive power.

It is a matter of choice though. Many have stumbled into the darkness and have used it for their gain. This has only led them to lose much of what made them human.

As part of my research, I have reached and attempted to understand religions and retain their spiritual powers as opposed to all that what man has added later on. I have delved deeper into the truth of that pure and wise word. I found the power of the word as the first thing ever mentioned in the Bible. This is no coincidence. I, of a Muslim faith, saw the truth in every religion I have read, felt the love shared in every story and anecdote, and I knew that at some point, all spiritual texts and lore converge into that one focal point; the simple act of loving unconditionally.

You might tell me that there are differences between religions, fundamental ones. I beg to differ! I am not interested in the analysis and overthinking of the word. The word just is, and the truth does not need to be dissected. The truth was written long before we were turned against each other, and believe me when I say, it all comes down to pure, unconditional love; the utterly pure power that has given rise to humankind. The spiritual part of religions is the finger pointing us into the right direction towards the truth that is inwardly found. I ask you to disregard the façades that have been created, not the way things are currently being portrayed. The *spiritual* foundations of religions are the absolute truth, let that sink in.

If you want to be the present and live in the present, you are to understand the word, love the word and be the word. Once you step outside the boundaries set by your mind, you will see things more clearly. You will stand in awe before the simple being that a flower is, you will appreciate the immensity and depth of sea. Becoming the word will open your heart and soul to the universe's infinite power to perceive things as they are in their truth. Once you forego the mind, you will wake up every morning knowing that you truly see the sunlight, you truly see other Beings; truly see what is before you as it is, not as agreed on by society. People will always remain people, but their value and their potential will be revealed as your intuition grows in strength.

Mindfulness: Connection to The Present

There are numerous mindfulness techniques out there. I have tried figuring out what might work and might not work for me. But every time I felt that I was close enough to get a definitive answer, life happens. Not in a bad way, but life comes as a reminder that there are no set rules. The only ones that we live by are those that have been established as truth by society. This means that we are living a mirage; a collective mirage that keeps on adapting to human evolution.

Establishing a routine can help dampen the impact of stress and of society's interference. Examples of such habits include breathing exercises, yoga, any kind of alternative fitness, such as dance and physical activity. There is no magic pill that can keep us from dipping in our underworld, and there are no ways to qualitatively know if we are succeeding or not. Breathing exercises are a way to remind your body and brain that you are living in the present. Yoga, for instance, will help you strengthen your mind-muscle connection, not to mention improve the overall energy flow. Workouts in general are your way to stay in the now and immobilize your mind's thoughts by focusing on the movement; it is another form of meditation that allows you to break old thought patterns.

Tip: Whenever you are doing breathing exercises, think of the air freely traveling in and out of your lungs. Feel it expanding your lungs and refreshing your cells. Upon exhalation visualize their air exiting your body through your mouth and nose; make it your central focal point in such a way as to anchor yourself. Visualize your in-breath as fresh and positive and then imagine releasing that stale air along with all that is holding you back.

Breathing techniques have been used for thousands of years by monks. It is quite common to focus on breathing since it allows the person doing the exercise to recognize the space between and in such a way as to lengthen the space between the two. This is another way to say that you can control your reaction to whatever is happening in your environment. An immediate reaction is not necessarily needed, so practicing mindfulness stretches the brain's ability to revisit the stimulus, dissect it and craft a wiser response.

It is quite on point to call such practices as *mindfulness* exercises as they put the mind in the spotlight. By increasing awareness of our mind's activity and patterns of behavior, we acquire a better view of what we are supposed to understand. It is like watching a predator from afar, studying its moves and slyly attacking it. All it takes is around five to twenty minutes each day to start noticing results. I do propose several steps that will help you get immediate results.

> ♦ Take a few deep and slow breaths focusing on relaxing your body and mind. This can be practiced before sleeping or upon waking in the morning.
> ♦ Intently focus on that is happening within and immobilize your emotions by observing them without judgment.

♦ When in an intense situation, and you feel like you are not able to cope, take some time out. Go for a short walk. It is a cross-crawl exercise, it will activate both sides of the brain, hence making you more aware of the way your thoughts are going. It will also provide you with a better understanding of the situation. This will expand your thought processes to understand your emotions and have a better response.

♦ Stand in a place where you can relax your eyes. An example of this would be by looking at the horizon, the mountains or greenery. Allow your eyes to wander and to relax. You are moved by muscles and will require some rest from time to time.

♦ When you feel like you are reaching a flight or fight reaction, start counting backwards. Count intently and slowly, making deliberate movements to give your counting a certain cadence. One way to do this is by counting down from 10 to 0, telling yourself that you will feel better as you get closer to number 0. It is a kind of self-hypnosis or guided self-meditation.

♦ Always allow your breath to expand your diaphragm. Shallow breath can trick the brain into thinking that you are in a dire situation, which would cause you more distress. Allow your breath to expand your belly. You can place your hands on either side of your belly to become more aware of the movement. Try to breathe out slower than you breathe in to support the parasympathetic nervous system.

There are various eye exercises that help you reduce eye strain and improve eyesight. Be committed to giving all parts of your body enough care.

> ◆ A few good techniques are blinking for one minute to relax your eyes and regulate blood flow.
>
> ◆ Focus on one point and rotate your head from side to side/up and down while keeping that point in view. This is a stretching exercise for your eye muscles and increases blood circulation inside your eyes. Do this exercise for 30 to 60 seconds.
>
> ◆ Move your eyes left and right, up, and down for 60 seconds.
>
> ◆ Close your eyes for a while to help your photoreceptors rest. This is said to improve eyesight if practiced every day during your free time. Think of something pleasant that you want to do or usually like to do. Do this for 30 seconds.

By practicing mindfulness, you will first start to feel more at ease and more confident. You will tap into your latent ability to *create* emotions such as compassion and love. This does not mean that you will be faking it, but you will be able to utilize your brain in ways you have never dreamed of. In more scientific terms, you will control your brain's activity. You will be able to calm your brain or fire up your neurons on demand.

Further, you will be able to start mastering your own mind, hence validating Buddha's definition of enlightenment as the "end of suffering." Your body will start healing itself from within. There is a whole host of meditation types; sports can even be included in this category thanks to the imposed focus on the breath, and on a certain number of actions that are to be exercised with precision. Prayer is another whereby you intently focus on scriptures and a set of prayers or mantras. But not all meditations are mindfulness ones. I am only asking you to focus on the simple act of breathing. That's all.

Mindfulness is very much like a muscle; you can train it to become stronger. The more you focus your attention, the better the result over time.

In recent years, I have been introduced to horse riding. This beautiful discipline was very therapeutic on several levels as it requires much attention. Some studies have viewed being around horses as another form of mindfulness exercise.

How is riding a horse or being around
horses related to mindfulness?

Riding a horse requires lots of control and being mindful of your own feelings and those of the beautiful creature you are riding. Horses are highly limbic creatures, meaning that they are largely flight animals, or in other terms, animals with a highly alert emotional system. Horses can sense a person's emotional state and react; accordingly, tension will trigger a violent reaction, while being in control will give rise to a beautiful experience. On a more personal note, the more time I spent riding horses, the more my posture changed, my back got stronger, and my mental state became more resilient. Horse-riding is a beautiful challenge and an opportunity to learn self-control, which is a crucial part of self-mastery.

By being mindful of yourself and of another being, you expand your brain's capacity for attention; you access a higher level of consciousness.

Debunking Meditation

You might have heard that you must empty your mind while meditating. But doing so is not beneficial; this is closer to avoidance than to allowing your brain and body to cope and react to stimuli in the most proper way. Mindfulness requires attention to stay within. After spending so much time at the hospital and looking for answers from specialists, the realization that I need to pay attention to what my body is saying hit me right in the face. I did not want to see my symptoms fade away and resurface. I wanted my body to fully heal from the core, I no longer wanted to treat symptoms, I wanted to find and heal what was ailing me. Allow me to elaborate. I have spent countless hours ruminating, procrastinating, and overthinking. And despite the various attempts to understand what is happening to my wife, my child and me, my attention was slipping away. I did not know what my mind was doing in the background. In fact, it was having a ball torturing me and creating a reality that I did not want. I have become its slave and was being dragged around by the stimuli around me. I lost the connection between my mind and body.

When I then started practicing mindfulness, my mind fought back as hard as it could. I felt restless and I did not want to sit and allow my body to take in all that oxygen. But practice makes perfect, and I was able to fathom what it means to pull your attention inwardly. It felt like I was restoring a piece of my being back to where it belonged. This let me become aware of my bubbling reactions especially during the time my third child was at the hospital fighting all kinds of infections with lowered immunity. I had become irritable and succumbed to the most poisonous of cycles. Mindfulness was my tool to look at my feelings and be aware of how my body and brain are reacting. Becoming the awareness behind the feeling became an exercise that I truly cherish. I was able to look at those passing feelings, know their nature, their causes and decide on the best course of action. Those feelings and I became acquainted with each other; they became visitors rather than invading entities.

I invite you to start applying mindfulness to anything and everything you do. Eat and be mindful of what you are eating, enjoy the taste, the texture. Walk and feel your muscles contract and release, look around feeling how colors and shapes intertwine. You can apply mindfulness to every little thing you do, hear, see, smell or touch, which will later morph into a routine or habit that you will enjoy. You will enjoy enjoying your quotidian actions.

Religions all have some foundation in the art of meditation. If you look at what the early scriptures mention and how they mention it, you will certainly find that it is an extended hand reaching out to your being. And just like any discipline, meditation is not a one-size-fits-all activity; on the contrary, it is a beautifully personal and intimate act whereby you shed all the burdens by acknowledging them and by knowing that you can handle all that you are going through. Despite the overarching aim of meditation, each type will ready your body, mind and being for a specific set of activities that are to follow, be it sleep, work, dance, or just enjoying a relaxing day.

There are around nine types of meditation, the first of which is mindfulness meditation. This one is based on Buddhist teachings and has been widely adopted in western countries. Mindfulness meditation is a perfect tool to unlearn judging; you simply watch your emotions and thoughts pass as though they are objects. All you are asked to do is to observe them, understand them and make it your mission to expand your consciousness beyond the normal human framework to engulf what *seemed* too heavy to bear. In order to properly exercise this type of meditation, you will have to focus on a specific object or preferably your breathing hence combining concentration and awareness. You can practice this type of meditation alone or using guides found online or offline.

The second type of meditation is spiritual meditation, which is what we are used to in the Middle East. For those who are not very familiar with my culture, we are very fond of frankincense, sage and cedar scents, which are widely used in religious rituals along with contemplating prayers in silence or focusing on establishing a connection with the higher power.

Focused meditation is the third form that I would like to mention here. It involves using a certain anchor to stay in the moment. A common practice involves the use of beads to tame the mind and not allow it wander.

The next form is called movement meditation. I am fond of this type of meditation as it includes walking in the woods or connecting with your environment through the gentle movement. It usually allows your brain to develop better problem-solving skills especially through walks and cross-crawl motions that involves synchronization between the two hemispheres of your brain. My wife and I take my children out on walks and allow them to let out some steam, but also ask them to try and keep their quiet as a way to train them for this meditation. Yet, I assure you, it is not always a success as their energies spike, and we end up guffawing as we chaotically run through the woods or gallop through them on horseback. It is very important to understand that some days meditation will be easy, others your mind will fight you and throw some mean right hooks. But commitment and perseverance are two potent weapons against this foe.

The next two types of meditation are very similar, which are the Mantra and transcendental meditations. The former usually requires the repetition of the "Om" sound, which is said to be the original sound of the universe and incorporates the very essence of reality itself. The latter is more flexible and requires a mantra or sound that is specific to every person.

Progressive relaxation meditation is also known as the body scan. It allows the person to focus on parts of the body in a specific order and to relax the muscles, hence fending off tension. What is interesting in progressive relaxation is that it sometimes involves the tightening of muscles first followed by their relaxation, not to mention the annexation of subtle visualization of waves rocking the body and massaging it. I recommend this before bedtime as it is the best way to soundly fall asleep.

The next type of meditation is an amazing one. It is based on love and kindness and is called so as it requires one to open up to receiving love from others. It usually helps those bottling up feelings of loneliness, anger, resentment, etc. Receiving love is a great way to heal and is even a better way to expand one's own emotional spectrum by opening up to feelings of compassion, kindness and unconditional love.

This last technique is one of the most powerful means to rid your mind of its weapon and it called visualization meditation. It entails using your mind's eye to visualize relaxing scenery. I recommend you do this daily for about 20 minutes; results will be beyond your expectations.

Purpose, Vision, Passion

"The purpose of life is not to be happy. It is to be useful, to be honorable, to be compassionate, to have it make some difference that you have lived and lived well." Ralph Waldo Emerson

Human beings gather, socialize, love to interact and share. Have you ever wondered why you are unhappy with your life? Have you ever had the feeling that you have wasted so much time that procrastination hits you right in the face? Not only procrastination, but also a sort of a disappointment, which is relatively worse than any other feeling. Then it hits you even harder, that feeling that you don't know what your life is all about.

Talking about purpose and vision got me thinking back on my childhood, adolescence, and adult life. It had me scrutinizing who I was and who I am today. My brain started pragmatically analyzing the decisions I have made, I retraced some of my steps, traced back others and even went back to some of my writings from my early years. I had kept a few notebooks filled with thoughts, analyses of some situations and recollections of a number of incidents. This was enough for me to recreate a clear enough image of my previous self that led to my present truth. All I know is that by doing so, I have come to understand that life's vision and purpose are based on five basic points, which are:

- ◆ Who I was
- ◆ What I did
- ◆ Who I did it for
- ◆ What I wanted or needed
- ◆ What I got out of it

It's not a hard task, is it? You can learn your life's purpose by thinking and revisiting these five points. This would take you around a few minutes to cover this Rule of Five, or it might stretch for around thirty minutes as some of the answers require you to think back on some of the most important stages that you have gone through. But promise yourself that you will do your best and will objectively go back in time.

Going back in time was the most beneficial thing I had ever done. It was not a means to regret things I have said and done, it was not even close to making me feel bad about myself; I felt out of my comfort zone, and despite my mind's numerous attacks and attempts to keep me in its loop or loops, that slight discomfort at the start of this process told me that I was on the right track.

If revisiting past self doesn't feel uncomfortable, or at least, it does not allow you to see yourself as yourself in that time – without filters – then you have not broken all the lies that you have been taught.

You are surely familiar with the renowned novel entitled *A Christmas Carol* by Charles Dickens, and if you are not, I advise you to read it as it is indispensable in so many ways. Ebenezer Scrooge, the protagonist is representative of our mind or of the person overrun by the mind's attacks and control, he is the epitome of the person who suffers, yet blames his own suffering on the others. You will find him lacking empathy, love, generosity, and humanity to sum it up. Yet, this gorgeous story includes a superb twist in which three spirits take Scrooge onto three respective trips; the first being back to the past, where he saw his younger and fresh self, revisited old places he loved, seen people he was attached to and re-felt some of his aches and pangs. This first stage was uncomfortable, and he even refused to look unto some of his memories which shed light on his transformation from a person connected to the universe and to life, to a shriveled up little mind. The second spirit took him on a flight across town, showing him how others are living the moment, how happiness can be found in this actual moment. Look at yourself reading now, your brain is activated, you are taking my words and allowing them to sink in, the same thing happened to Scrooge as he saw the narrative of the present moment unfold.

The third and crucial phase of his transformation required him to look at the future and see how his actions affected those around him. The grim spirit of the future showed him that by remaining disconnected from the universe and from life, his presence on his realm had negative side effects, including the death of a sweet, sick boy who happened to be his employee's son. The story serves our being on a variety of levels and allows it to expand thinking in ways it never thought it was able to.

A Christmas Carol is one of those avant-garde novels especially in the time of the "great industrialization" that saw the human need for connection and reconnection. It was one of the earliest works that consider the question of awareness and the impact of it has on those that have been living their lives away from purpose and vision. This story is the best example that I have found thanks to the author's genius to illustrate a technique that I will reveal later that eventually led Scrooge to change his attitude.

Our lives have become so hectic. Everything around is racing so fast as though time is a tyrant who wants to outrun even the swiftest of us. During my business endeavors, I almost lost everything. I was faced with lawsuits and had to deal with lawyers, judges, and a whole lot of paperwork. As I saw my world almost collapse, I felt knew that my vision of what a happy life was distorted and based on what I was taught. I only wanted to succeed, build a career, create things, and maximize profit. I was a businessman after all, and my vision was narrow. I was not in touch with the self or being. I can almost say that business took over most of my life. Nothing is better than a dip into the underworld to feel the fire and face some kind of ultimatum. The burns that this dip left on me, which were obviously more on the emotional and psychological levels, have yet to heal and dissolve. I can still feel them. it's not pain that I am going through, not the least, but they act as a reminder that the cycle I had gone through was beneficial. I learned that my vision of a happy life was not related to the mundane, and my purpose, which I thought was to be a businessman, a successful one at that, was way beside what the universe had in store for me.

After waking up from my spiritual and mental coma, I discovered that my life's purpose was to leave a legacy for my children, all people in my life and for you. These words that are pouring from my brain right now, are the product of a lot of nights and days of meditation, reading, prayer and love.

My story, observation and analyses are yours for the taking; they are the blueprint to becoming who you really are. Reach your truth and you shall live the happiest life. Think beyond the limitations that society has set for you. You are not society, and you are your own support.

The road to self-mastery is one that requires much dedication; it might be difficult at first, but once you start practicing with intent. If you do the following exercises putting all your life force into it, visualizing who you want to be and who you can be. Please allow me to guide you a little further into the wonders of purpose of vision.

The first step that will take you closer to your purpose and vision is visualizing your final moments on this earth. Visualize yourself on your deathbed. Scary or gloomy as it may seem, this first and crucial step will put you out of your comfort zone. There is nothing better than forcing your mind to live a moment of death, which is literally take you to a mental near-death experience and purify your mind, brain, and soul. It will bring clarity to your thoughts and motivate you to get back what was originally yours. I know that there are lots of superstitions regarding thinking of one's own death, but these are just limiting beliefs to keep from reliving moments of lucidity and purity that are akin to those you have experienced and forgotten at the time of your own birth and early childhood. I ask you to become the infant you were.

I would like you to sit in a comfortable position, have everything around you ready, from a glass of water to your phone or any other tablet or computer so that you could record the changes you are feeling. You are not required to make any effort while writing or typing or recording your voice (in case you are comfortable doing so). Now visualize yourself as being able to see your body lying there, surrounded by every single person you can conjure up. Gather all those faces and press them together around what looks like your lifeless body and allow three of them to start sharing things about you. You should however choose people from different backgrounds and preferably from different stages of your life and reflect upon what you would like them to say. Imagine them talking about your life but in terms of how you would like them to perceive you. Think in terms of the legacy you are leaving behind, the impression you left, the way you acted and how people saw it. Guide someone to develop purpose and vision briefly.

> ◆ Think about your death bed or look back on your funeral as though it has taken place. Imagine three people (each one from family, friends, business) and imagine what you would like them to talk about you. What would your legacy be?
>
> ◆ Set your purpose in life based on that and set your objectives based on what you want to hear as the one who has passed on.
>
> ◆ Set a plan and start with something.
>
> ◆ Set a concrete daily/weekly routine, which goes into changing habits and establishing good routines.

Passions are what connects us with the world. They keep us awake. Finding your passion in life is crucial to uphold your mental health. Being passionate about something feels like being in love with whatever you are working on, whatever you are attracted to. The thing or hobby you are passionate about should make you light up whenever you talk about it. It is impossible to find a human being without a passion. Many claim that they do not have a particular passion; they live a stale life that is devoid of purpose and of any color; however, such claims hold no truth as all humans have a certain passion or at least something that attracts them. It is just that they are not aware of that makes them feel this way; they are not aware of the moment they connect to something and enjoy it to the fullest.

Allow yourself to be passionate, let go of what society might say about you. Do what makes you feel inspired and good while letting go of any commentary that you might receive. What's good for you works for you, just be aware of your passions, make them a part of your daily life, allow yourself to enjoy that sacred time, become the creator you are. Once you do that, the energy that courses through us whenever we are passionate about something awakens the latent creative powers that we have.

Passion is another component of mental health. A healthy brain and a healthy mind are inspired. Have you ever woken up with so much energy you felt you can do anything? Have you ever felt that your ideas are flowing ever so freely and happily? This is because you are mentally aligned with the energy around you, and once you synchronize your thoughts, which are energy too, with the right frequencies, you will soar.

Being in sync with the world feels like you are in love and overflowing with inspiration and passion.

It is beautiful how we can become part of everything through passion and inspiration. We might be ascribing very large concepts to just two words. But I believe that by understanding our role and allowing our brains to fathom the intricacies of this universe through what we love; we will be opening up to much more powerful tools that were already at our disposal. With this done, your aura will change, and you will effortlessly spread positivity around.

Go find what you love, what you are passionate about, what inspires you. Talk to people, listen to their words, listen to their unsaid words, watch their faces and expressions; the world is full of big and small things that will bring out your creative juices and make you the creator you are born to be. Passion and inspiration are the embodiment of our divinity.

Once your life passions and inspiration take over, your problem-solving skills will reach new heights and your outlook on life will become much broader. Let that sink in.

Relationship with Limiting Beliefs

It is no coincidence that this part of the book comes right after Passion and Inspiration. The flow of the energy that I have been feeling while pouring my heart into this book has allowed me to scrutinize every idea and despite my pragmatic attempts to plan this book according to what seemed or looked only scientific, I believe that the flow of energy had driven me to accept some of the changes that my inner being requested.

As I stepped into Switzerland at the age of seven, I was faced with so many challenges. I did not speak the language, I was seen as an outsider, and children were rude to me. I was the dark entity that stepped into the Swiss scene. I had to face some bullying and my peers' limiting beliefs regarding my origins and especially my religion.

What was even adding to that challenge was the fact that my name was unfamiliar; it exacerbated the emotional aggression I was subjected to. In other words, I was bullied, just because I was different. Furthermore, as you might imagine, I had trouble applying to my first jobs and was expected to deploy more efforts to prove that I was better than other candidates. I do not wish to go into the inner workings of the human psyche, yet I know that all that is different can instigate such a reaction, but what about curiosity? Humans rely so much on the flight, fight, or freeze reaction without giving a thought to the fact that they are, in my specific case, dealing with another human being. If I were asked if I would change anything from my past, I wouldn't trade any moment away for another; I am more emotionally intelligent thanks to these experiences, I am more resilient thanks to the picking and bullying, I am who I am thanks to the ups and downs that I thought would destroy me.

It's a wonder how collective views can act as a poison or as a remedy, yet it all depends on how you allow it to act within your system and how you allow your system to react to it. Everything is action and reaction, it is like chemistry, but the main difference here is that you can *create* rather than just mix the components and await the final product.

My move to Switzerland was the best thing that had happened to me, not because I would only enjoy peace and good education, but also discover how being different really feels. But this acceptance of my state as different required me to overcome a few hurdles, such as the feeling that I had something wrong with me, and that I was living on the margins of society. Such thoughts were just a blur in my mind, and I coveted being alone with myself. The most difficult part of my upbringing is dealing with two backgrounds and two cultures at the same time. We had retained our Lebanese customs at home but had to adapt to the external world. I had my micro society and my macro society how each had their limiting beliefs. Those limiting beliefs were transferred to me, I struggled with them, and they held me back for a while. If I am to depict it in a clearer way, it would a sort of cultural limbo. I was a hybrid with a fundamentally different view of those around me. My lens a wider in some respects and narrower in some, but the experience was an eye opener.

Yet, as I grew older, I was able to put these fallacies on the table and dissect them. I could see how my Lebanese roots were chaining my thoughts and brain, while being pushed away by my host culture allowed for a clearer vision; I became more flexible, and this change pushed me to adapt by developing tools and views that were focused on empathy. We are born empathetic; babies cry when others are upset or crying around them. they feel the energy and they share it. If they are happy, the scream and giggle without trying to hide that beautiful force they have within. As we grow older, we start ornamenting ourselves, we start working as per society's expectations, smiling less because others might not take us seriously, we start laughing less, the things that touch us lessen in potency. I was obviously born very empathetic, I grew up amid bombings and I was told that I cried very little, but my face told the whole story. I admit, that during my teenage and adult years, I have lost my empathy to a certain extent; what with business life taking me over and my numerous occupations, I felt some sort of depersonalization as I grew year after year. I did not feel as though I was growing old, but I felt something was missing and that a crucial part of myself has fallen into a coma; a coma that I induced.

I started looking inwardly without knowing what to actually look for. It was a time of discovery, recovery, and self-understanding. Little did I know that losing one's own empathy can lead to a robot-like life. As I opened long-shut doors in my brain, I stumbled across a memory of my mother when we were back in Beirut. I remembered how her face used to contort in painful expressions whenever she heard someone was wounded, missing or dead. The first few times I recalled these memories, I felt as though something within me was moving, like a latent power, but it felt paralyzed. This feeling of powerlessness bothered me a lot because it felt as though your dentist had used a little too much anesthetic and your face felt like drooping, although was not the case. This spin through my emotions and memories felt like a roller coaster ride, it brought about some anxiety as well since it was all unfathomable. My mind was in full control of my life and made me feel as though I had to prove myself to a society that looked down on me.

This was my opportunity to learn from the differences and to understand the inner dynamics of a society that has lived in peace for as long as I remember. As I delved into the understanding of those differences, I became aware that my acceptance of myself was the only option for my being thrive. I realized and became aware of the fact that I did not need to convince anybody of the power of my own presence, it was not my job to teach anybody what to do or how to see the truth, but I understood that by being myself and accepting myself first, my presence will be of worth, not only for those in my immediate entourage, but also as a speck in this universe, a powerful speck of humanity.

With this came empathy and my adult life was ruled for the most part with my endeavor to realize unlearn the poisonous thoughts and limiting beliefs that have plagued my being for so long. So, after accepting myself, loving myself and allowing unconditional love to enter my life, I felt connected to others and to the universe. I thus created my own reality, my own family, my own environment, and my very own universe. I was allowed blessings to lighten my life and I was able to bless my being with the contentment and happiness it is worthy of.

We all face limiting beliefs every single second of our days. We negotiate based on those limiting beliefs, talk, walk, breathe, and think based on what our shackles dictate. The mind loves these games and adores restricting the being with the power of the word. Imagine the power that this manmade creation holds over the divine, just because we grant it access to our core. One of the experiences that stuck in my mind is that of a client who thought that what he believed was true; other people's feelings and opinions did not matter as he was willingly blinding his being and giving leeway to his mind to exert its negative influence. He was the epitome of a person plagued by limiting beliefs.

Limiting beliefs can be broken, but this requires courage and dedication, you will have to be very aware of what they are. You might think that you will be judged for talking in a certain way, disliked for walking in a certain way, betrayed by your closest friends or just assume that you will never be worthy of anything good.

Limiting beliefs can be broken, but this requires courage and dedication, you will have to be very aware of what they are. In order to know how to break the shackles of limiting beliefs, you must at least have a basic understanding of their categories.

Limiting beliefs can usually be personal ones that are used on certain personal experiences leading the person to develop fears and blocks that hinder any kind of progress. The second type of limiting beliefs are those related to one's one genetic background, one's own ideas, how one is created and the fallacy that all behavior is hereditary. Such a major fallacy usually pushes individuals into psychosomatic disorders, addiction or worse as they think they will be carrying the same behavior code as their parents. The third type of limiting beliefs are excuses used to halt any course of action by fear of failure. Fourth come social circles and how they influence the individual by creating a copy of the person and instilling certain ideas about them in their minds. The fifth type encompasses the fourth one and is related to the whole society that sometimes creates impossible standards that usually lead to limiting beliefs among certain groups that trickle down to individuals. The last limiting belief is related to religion and how it paints a false image of the world. This last fallacy is usually very dangerous as it belittles the divine and fits it into a very limited and earthly frame.

You might think that you will be judged for talking in a certain way, disliked for walking in a certain way, betrayed by your closest friends or just assume that you will never be worthy of anything good. With these ideas floating around your mind, ask your being: "who told you so?"

Do not beat yourself up for thinking this way since it was never your intention to be limited or to limit others. Mind you, you are the product of your environment. Yet, you are the only creature on this earth, if not this universe, equipped with awareness; a powerful tool that will drill through the blackness of ignorance and let the light in. You are therefore invited to identify your limiting beliefs. Take a pen and paper and start writing down your opinion regarding certain things, people, groups, society as a whole. Regard these with skepticism. Think in terms of *true* and *untrue*.

Then comes the real work; ask yourself whether you have proof that these are real claims. Whether they are well supported, if you have always thought the same way, if you change your point of view, would anything change, if such a belief helps me reach my objective or is a hindrance, if I put myself in the other person's shoes, would my view be altered.

Once you are done with these questions, and I am sure you can find so many additional ones to answer and challenge, you can start by adopting a more open mindset towards all that seems like passed-down judgments and making a habit of not falling into the same old patterns of behavior. This is very similar to working out and conditioning your body to reach an acceptable fitness level before hitting the actual grueling exercise bout. In other words, you can start practicing mindfulness and awareness by knowing, first, that your mind is pushing towards those fallacies. The good habit will eventually overcome the bad one and you will find that your consciousness has expanded since old stressors are no longer there.

The realization that I can change my life has allowed me to remove all the toxicity that has built up over the years. I have mentioned that I felt like an outsider; a person set on the margins of society. Yet, as times went by and thanks to my upbringing, my automatic reaction was to challenge all that society threw at me, I built companies, watched some of them crumble, then built others with the same power and unwavering intent.

When you challenge those toxic ideas, your mind will be boggled and despite its various and sporadic attacks, you will be able to win the battles and the war through awareness and mindfulness.

Act When You Should

Take a moment and think of instances where an idea crossed your mind. It might have been a good or bad idea, regardless, let us not categorize it. Beyond the fact that an idea can be good or bad, have you ever considered your brain's response to your thoughts, and on a deeper level, have you ever considered your body's response to your brain's response to your thoughts?

Most of us would be sitting somewhere, then, just like a lightning strike, something comes to mind, a goal, an objective or just a need. This is normal and we all have ideas or things we need to do throughout the day, yet we sometimes decide – willingly or not – to procrastinate and nag about it. There is a very simple explanation to this, and it will make a whole lot of sense once I am done. So right after reading this part, please take a moment and rethink your thoughts, and your body's/brain's reactions to thoughts.

This part is all about taking action right when you get the idea. I would like to emphasize the importance of valuing good ideas that would have an added value, such as deciding to hit the gym despite feeling, or thinking that you feel, tired. Another idea would be to go for a walk, to finish that paper, research a topic, learn something new, etc.

Your brain, which will then be undergoing a stressful moment of indecisiveness, will only need five seconds to either accept the idea and start implementing it or kill it altogether. The five-second rule does exist and can be the solution to your indecisiveness moments, not to mention that it can train you to start taking action.

If you feel you are hesitating before tackling that project, or before heading out, count down from 5 to 1 to push yourself out from a state of stagnation, which will eventually turn into a cursed autopilot ride. You can make your brain work better for you by telling yourself that you are 'starting' something and focusing on the idea that you can do so much more. This also applies to whenever you are in a stressful situation. I mean, we all go through those moments when we are about to lash out in anger or allow our stress to get the best of us. Don't feel guilt about your feelings, they are normal and you are a human being. Yet, the way you react to those feelings is what transcends you. Instead of lashing out, use that above 5-second rule and breathe. Counting to five or down to one does not have to be obvious to others, just let your brain slip into the counting activity, which will take it to a better place, hence pulling the brakes on your stress, anger, and any other negative emotion you are experiencing.

Remember that when you start counting, this does not mean that you are counting down towards the moment you will explode. On the contrary, you are counting in a mindful way, allowing your Being to consider and weigh its options and find the best way to deal with the situation.

Gratitude and Awe

Gratitude and awe seem to be taken lightly in today's society. This statement doesn't come as blame, rather an observation of the current status quo. We tend to live our lives as though we are immortal; we take things for granted, forget the importance of those whom we love and love us back. This is why many people say that they cannot live with themselves; they can't take this life anymore. Why? Because they feel they do not belong.

Humans developed and evolved this realm and are meant to move to the next. I do not wish to consider the future; it is not my intention, and it will never provide any kind of specific and true answer. But I believe that we are, now, part of the present moment, and there is nothing more powerful than the present moment. We belong to the now and looking around us in this particular moment; we see that everything around us is wonderful. All religions seek to instill a feeling of awe in us. If taken in the right context, this feeling of awe is what any major religious figure called for.

"Truly I tell you, unless you change and become like little children, you will never enter the kingdom of heaven." (Matthew 18:3)

Some translations have added the expression *turn from your sins* to the quote above. This has come to be misinterpreted by many scholars and religious figures. Sins what we have been taught in the classical sense. Taking another person's life, and/or your own, stealing, hurting others in any way, be it mentally, emotionally, or physically, fall under the category of sin. The lack of awe and gratitude has led humans astray; the feeling that the grass is always greener somewhere else is the cause of all those abominable actions.

Feeling grateful and living in awe allow you to perceive the truth of things. Gratitude is more powerful than any ailment, more powerful than loneliness and more powerful than any other negative emotion. Gratitude creates a beautiful interpersonal spacetime among people as I like to call it. Gratitude has even been scientifically proven to alter one's state of mind. It engages parts that are deeply located in the prefrontal cortex. Of course, there are a number of steps to reach gratitude, such as not comparing yourself to others, staying in the past and ruminating about the future. This can be depicted as letting your mind run loose in the confines of your being. As part of my experience with psychotherapists and patients, being concerned with what other people think, as well as worrying about the future, among other things instigate several negative and paralyzing feelings. In order to restore the balance, we have found that nudging the patient towards a feeling of gratitude led to the desired end, which is to live in gratitude and in the present moment.

Science has proven that practicing gratitude has a direct impact on neurons; it alters brain structures and creates new pathways that are strengthened with practice. Just like any other habit, the practice of seeing the good in what you have will allow you to create a positive pattern in all other situations, hence allowing you to see the glass half full regardless of the predicament you are facing.

Gratitude, just like physical activity, releases dopamine into the bloodstream; hence spiking your motivation, bringing about pleasure, spiking your attention and allowing you to enjoy life as it is. Alongside dopamine, serotonin – the happiness hormone – is also released. The scientific benefits of gratitude do not stop here. FMRI scans have shown that expressing gratitude activates the prefrontal cortex; the part of the brain that is linked to decision-making and leaning. It is therefore of great importance to express gratitude and not just feel grateful for something. Make it a habit to verbalize this feeling, hence allowing your brain to release all those beautiful chemicals into your bloodstream.

On another level, living in a state of gratitude and awe puts you in touch with your inner self/child. It allows your inner eye – some call it your third eye – to really perceive what is out there and not just what has been limited by our human mind's way of describing things. Rain, sun, sky, man, woman become one and in the absence of all things human, the beauty that is within that wholeness shines through to you. What is even more interesting in this state of mind is that you become synchronized with the universe through your environment, imagine yourself being plugged into some kind of Universal Serial Bus or USB port, and receiving all that love as freely as you can imagine.

Can you elaborate on the last idea please?

The concept of being plugged into the universe has been described as vibrating on the same frequency as everything around you. when you tap into the truth of the being, the truth of all things around you, the concept of good and bad dissolve, and with this, your mind becomes confused. You might be confused right now as you try to fathom the intricacies of such a mode of thinking and action; however, instead of trying to rationalize everything, I bring you the only solution and that is to dissociate yourself from the mind and its attempt to make you think that you are not who you really are. I invite you to stop trying to scrutinize these explanations in a pragmatic way for a state of mind such as this one cannot be really understood. It is rather through muting the mind's noise that you will fathom how it *feels* to be in that state of sync.

Trying to mute the mind will cause uproar within. Put up a good fight. The mind will play card after card, and when you reach the final blow, it will do its best and worst to stop you. This reminds me of a character in a series called *The Good Place* and the way philosophy and psychology intertwined with comedy.

The Key to Love Yourself

There is no magical pill. As much as I would like to claim that I can give you the ultimate solutions to life's mysteries, which are beautiful in every way, I believe that the key to wellbeing and to a great mental health resides in the idea of self-worth. Self-worth, as opposed to self-importance, stems from self-love, self-care, understanding one's own feelings emotions and being aware of them. The most beautiful thing about self-worth is that it is unwavering once you establish a connection with it; it is timeless strength and the basis upon which your self-esteem is built. Despite the fact that self-esteem is mostly influenced by external factors your feeling of self-worth is a crucial cornerstone for self-mastery and a life in balance.

As you might have noticed, I have shared some of the most intimate parts of my life as a means to get you involved in my journey. When I mention that the key to reaching self-mastery is through self-worth and self-esteem, I literally mean that you will have to look at yourself in that mirror and verbally express gratitude for being who you are. Another point that I cannot stress enough is to stop pleasing others while forgetting yourself. Stop being a people pleaser because you'd be doing whatever others ask of you, regardless of whether you like it or not. Where's the fun in that? Where's the fairness in that to your Being? People pleasers usually take it a little too far and find themselves anxious and upset while being emotionally depleted. Nobody wants to be emotionally depleted. Put your needs first; they are your priority.

If people find you pleasant and agreeable whenever you put them first, it is because their minds were able to see the naïve energy that you are emitting. Those minds were able to see through the deed into the inability to say no. falling into the people-pleasing pattern is toxic to you and my advice to you is to find what works for you first.

If you have trouble knowing whether you are a people pleaser, the below points can shed light on some of the traits that make you so.

- ◆ You cannot say "no."
- ◆ You always worry about what others might be saying about you.
- ◆ You feel guilty for refusing to do something.
- ◆ You are afraid to turn out selfish in your behavior.
- ◆ You do things you don't like.
- ◆ You look for other people's approval.
- ◆ You keep on apologizing at times you needn't.
- ◆ You see every little mistake or bad thing as your fault.
- ◆ You forget that you have needs.
- ◆ You do not share you differing opinions by fear of looking arrogant or selfish.

You will have to shed the various depictions that you carry around and that other people use to categorize you. You are beyond categorization and being so will lead you to towards something we all crave; happiness.

I cannot write about happiness as a sole entity, just as experts cannot mention one kind of vitamin, but rather focus on the fact that they come in various complexes in order to properly function.

I feel the need to mention one very important point at this stage; extremes. Falling into the extreme forms of self-worth and self-love will certainly lead to the poisoning the sensitive – yet powerful – Being. The manifestation of this poison will be through narcissism, which we will have to avoid at all costs.

Narcissists may believe that they are more important than others and that they are the perfect benchmark. Narcissists usually lack empathy and consideration for those around them, meaning that they do not feel with others. Narcissists are usually described as extremely bossy, patronizing and resist any kind of change that might affect their behavior. People with Narcissistic Personality Disorder or NPD for short, take the slightest criticism to heart, and all kinds of remarks become a personal matter to them. In other terms, they usually react very badly, and it will be noticeable to everyone around them.

Creating a beautiful life through self-love is almost guaranteed, and this form of unconditional love, whereby you express gratitude for everything that you are, from the color of your hair to your height, health, form, etc. This will open the doors to the cosmos's greatest powers and to opportunities you never thought you would be able to get. Such opportunities might translate into new jobs, better quality time with yourself, better relationships, and ultimately a mix of all that makes life ever so good.

You will find no need to justify why you are happy and will live in a state of contentment, awe, and wonder. Despite the various problems that we usually tend to fight, making amends with them is what trickles down from having a constantly *smiling* being. This means that by allowing your body to love itself and the true vision of how it looks and feels, your inner being will start to expand and take over. This is no magic trick; numerous individuals have struggled with body dysmorphic disorder and have let their minds taint the beauty they have right under their noses. We tend to forget that beauty is idiosyncratic, and that what is photoshopped onto magazines is nothing close to the truth. This takes us back to the idea that we are to live our truth no matter what!

I call upon your Being and I call upon your awareness of your Being to accept yourself as you are. I am by no means forcing any idea upon you, but to merely accept your physical self, accept that you might be going through tough times, good times, accept that you might have a spectrum of feelings rushing through you, and with that I invite you to love every little molecule that makes you, *you*. Verbally express love and make it your mission to radiate that love and happiness.

Won't I look a little crazy doing so?

By asking that question, you will be relaying to me the impact of society on our being and pointing out that we can still fall prey to that poisonous entity. Yet, no, there is nothing more beautiful than expressing gratitude to life coursing through your veins and through your inner being. You are a force, not some kind of small creature under the microscope. Genuinely loving yourself and cleansing your being from the toxicity that has plagued our modern and digital lives will lead to more love.

Happiness does not need justification, it's the only thing that comes out of love in all its forms and by loving yourself you usher your being into other forms of love.

SOCIAL HEALTH

Meaningful Connections

I would like to draw a major distinction between connections and relationships. I was about to write about meaningful relationships, but it dawned upon me that our human presence goes much more into the power of connection rather than the less broad concept of a relationship. I believe that connection includes relationships and with that in mind, I have come to understand some of the most fundamental interactions and ideas that I have come across. My aim is to provide tools to reach self-mastery, and what better way to reach this enlightened state than by understanding how we humans think and how such a process has evolved over time.

As humans we either connect or perish. Long before social media established itself as the overarching ruler of humanity and the major supporter of the man-made mind, connection was something else.

Looking at our primordial connection with nature; that vital relationship with the everlasting entity that the cosmos or universe has given us, I have settled for the idea that human beings need each other, yet this seems, not only cliché, but used and abused. Nature, our actual biological mother, from which we have emerged and evolved, is our primordial connection with our planet. I shall not go into prehistoric times but jump to eras where humans had developed enough awareness and attempted to unveil more knowledge based on their observations. From a shallow and straightforward perspective, the Greeks and then the Romans created their gods to embody natural phenomena. This idea had been around for ages; humans being afraid of floods, drought, lightning and so on, gave all these natural instances of power a human figure. We have turned the unknown into something approachable. We have turned a faceless and frightening thing into something familiar based on human beauty. With that ultimate form of physical beauty comes a connection with nature and the reestablishment of what had been lost for a while. After leaving the wilderness, and building cities, man needed to reconnect with nature, and so gods came to be created in his own image. This connection with nature came through the human body and the human understanding of the body. Throwing thunder bolts is surely out of the question but equating our physique with the divine came as a first step towards establishing a beautiful connection. The most interesting part in our evolution is that there are no signs that we have transitioned into this understanding in a gradual manner. In fact, civilizations seemed to have popped into the light in the blink of an eye, and the first connection that we had with nature was morphed into one with gods and their very human ways of thinking. Apart from Olympus and other human-like divine realms, other connections were established, and this time, such connections could be joined under one umbrella; the human-to-human link through storytelling and the creation of a social life. The darkness that used to envelope the world was lifted, to be replaced with the light of civilized thought. That connection had meaning, a deeper, yet lost meaning nowadays. This might sound a little grim, but we have lost the power of true relationships. This might not be the case of the 7 or 8 billion of us living across the globe, but the reality we are living in in these modern times has shifted our understanding of meaningful relationships from genuine love, compassion, empathy and understanding through direct contact to a counterfeit replica.

It is funny how everything that we used to regard as personal, private and intimate has come to be published everywhere and accessible to every single person on the planet. We get caught in a lie; a lie of happiness projected on a small piece of glass that lights up. But what is the true nature of our need for connection? Why does our dopamine spike every time we see our smartphones light up, vibrate or ring? We have transmuted our need for the original connection into something that is digital and foreign.

On Loneliness and Depression

Depression is the most misunderstood psychological or mental ailment. None of us really understand the mechanisms of what is clinically dubbed as depressive disorders. Diagnosable depression is more common than you think, you could have been or be right now in contact with people close to you suffering from such an ailment; however, as information is so readily available online, we tend to find patterns were there are none, and most of us label sadness as depression. If one is sad, this does not mean that they are suffering from a disorder. Professionals rely on a specific number of symptoms to diagnose someone with a depressive disorder, which includes sadness and emptiness on the emotional levels, as well as impaired mental processes and fatigue, among others, over a period of two weeks.

Why consider depression now? I would like to think of loneliness and depression as the most interconnected elements. I am not delving into psychology and the above information was meant to give minimal competence; however, when I come to think of loneliness, I remember clients that have gone through the rocky roads of depression. They spoke of sudden drops of energy, how they felt paralyzed over weeks at a time and lost interest in their usual activities. Depression burdened their Beings with thoughts of hopelessness and restricted their access to the power that awe, wonder and gratitude can bring.

Studies have shown that around 60% of individuals between 15 and 30 years old feel lonely, 26% of which are likely to die earlier. Those who are isolated and/or live alone even run a 32% increased risk of premature death. So, loneliness has a direct impact on life expectancy and happiness.

Loneliness is what the lack of proper connection feels like; it is very much akin to the accumulation of toxins in your system, yet it is very hard to flush out without proper exercise and diet.

Knowing who to connect with is undeniably the most crucial life lesson, for as you grow, your circle shrinks in size, but the quality of those who stay increases. The lack of awareness and living life in a blind fashion, without seeing the signs, will only keep our decisions questionable, hence keeping you in circles of people who are not actual friends, not even acquaintances, and at the very worse, emotional vampires who will feed on your weakness. Living in such a situation will lead to loneliness and to depression, then to various disabilities and physical illnesses that had started out just as psychosomatic symptoms.

The number of intimate people we tend to talk to has been decreasing since the eighties. Without proper connection, we feel that we are sinking into an abyss that is beyond our understanding because our brains are hardwired to live and connect. It is no wonder why so many teens have been committing suicide, why so many individuals – children, teens, and adults – feel so lonely and sad. We are lacking proper connection and this connection cannot be established without empathy, love, gratitude, awe and last, but definitely not least, putting down that phone and intently listening to what others are really saying.

For one, I try to bring humor and lightheartedness wherever I go. It is proven by science that humorous people are more likely to establish true connections with others because their aim is to bring joy to others. Being a human being is more than just eating, breathing, working, and sitting at home watching the series. Being human is being humane with ourselves, it is allowing the miracle of connection to take place, and it is allowing it to wash over us and to make it clear that we are nothing close to the machines that we have become.

I practice what I preach, and I love how I have my own field of experiment ready at home. In order to clearly see the impact of proper connection, I have established a set program for my children with the intent of bringing them the light of growth away from any limiting beliefs. This experiment, which has become a beautiful habit, revolves around having each one of us share three positive things we have experienced during our day.

At first, this was a little tough as we adults were a little focused on the tedious tasks that we wanted to accomplish, the nagging pains, the problems that we face and so on. Yet, as time passed by, our efforts bore fruit and the cycle of positive thinking became a habit. Finding positive things became easier and with that our children, who felt the power of positivity rise within us, wanted to tell us more positive things they have witnessed or experienced.

This all falls into our need for genuine connection, and with that tether linking us all, the current of positivity will allow us to shine. My children's eyes now glow up as they go into their frenzy of storytelling, and it is beautiful. The simplicity of establishing connection might scare most teens and adults, because we got so used to believing that all things ought to have some fine print hidden somewhere; some kind of price to pay. But being a *generator* of the positive current does not require anything but empathy and opening up the doors for others to feel your presence.

When Life Happens

I became aware of just how beautiful it was to share my gratitude and happiness with my wife and children. I became aware of the importance of understanding life's tough moments. My journey towards this state of understanding started off shortly before my son's hospitalization and resumed right after I had my heart attack. Me being in the intensive care unit (The ICU) was surreal and an eye-opener. I do not wish for anybody to be stuck in the ICU, but I believe that looking at it as a lesson has transcended this experience into the knowledge I have acquired and further developed today. At the time, I was running a venture capital firm; an investment company that assists startups and provides consulting services as well as business development for small businesses to reach their potential and objectives. The Swiss Financial Market Supervisory Authority suddenly swooped down on us with the assumption that our practice was illegal and that we needed further approvals to resume our activity as a financial institution.

My lawyers and I were under the impression that this is not the case. Following an exchange of emails, the FINMA closed down the company, and this was at the time where I had my breakdown and my heart attack. It was the start of a long and challenging road rigged with never-ending legal give and take. The fight which lasted six years at the highest court in Switzerland ended with us winning. A lot was lost during

156

these six years, but I shall not dwell on the material or financial, I shall only point out that it had put much of my connections in the limelight. This experience showed me the real connection I had with some of my closest friends and family members. It was enough for me to tap into my emotional intelligence. I became aware of the fact that people were less likely to enjoy my presence whenever I let worry and my mind's constant nagging run loose.

Living in a past state is surely not something our Being seeks to be trapped in. The future isn't either anything remarkable to look at. It is not! It's just what our minds are trying to calculate, it is not the truth. You might think that you are right, you might nail some of the details, but it is still an illusion. The present moment is all there is!

As we fought for our right to resume operations, my mind was taken further into the future and painting a rather grim image based on what was happening at the time. I was trapped…literally trapped and I couldn't get a hold of myself, hence the heart attack. Remember, your mind should be doing day-to-day *essential* tasks only. Once these tasks are completed, this mind; this superbly curious and envious mind – envious of the Being for the power it holds – should remain silent.

Going back to the concept of connections, the above experience has put me in a tight spot, a rather painful one, and it was not before long that I created a connection with my being and felt the present moment too. It felt like a truly blessed moment when things seemed to clear up and my vision, which was blurred by the numerous thoughts, was suddenly focused. My presence felt more organic and real to me and to others. The connection with my inner being and true reality was divine, and I could model it the way I wanted.

This first connection (with nature) is the basis of all that is to come. This is one of the pillars of self-mastery and will require much effort focused on understanding your inner being and listening to the true story behind its presence. If I am to explain what I mean, I would certainly refer to our modern-day life, which has become ever so absorbed by over-stimulating environments, all that is seemingly politically correct, concepts that are half baked and mind-ruled threads. Refusing such a life would certainly look like trying to amputate one of your limbs. But I am not asking you to do so, or to relinquish your interest in what has been introduced into our lives. Just like the very paradoxical question of dissociating yourself from your mind, I ask you to dissociate yourself from the man-made ideal of modern-day life; that claustrophobic and absurd disconnected connection with everyone around you. I am sure that you can sense that feeling of people being there, yet not there. Most individuals would be sitting in groups on their phones. That non-present presence severs the connection with those who are physically trying to connect with you.

The reality is that starting with our connection with nature has hardwired us to covet connections of all kinds regardless of their nature.

As humans, we seek connections and most of us try to find it in the form of a partner or a friend. This connection comes after we have established one with our original mother. Nature granted us so many strengths thanks to its challenges and careful selection of the fittest and through evolution.

Then came our need for interaction and connection with the equal, with other human beings. It is no wonder that many religions focus on group prayers, joining the faithful and praising those who live according to the laws of love and group support. I have always found living with others quite the joy. I have come to understand throughout my experience, on the professional level and on the persona level, that connecting with humans perfects our Beings. Of course, there remain exceptions to be seen and individuals and groups might bring about a cascade of negative events, yet the universe sends you all that you need based on your honed mental skills and talents.

I believe that it is by divine right that we ought to connect all together. In Christianity for example, the cross carries in its simple shape various meanings. Apart from being a torture and punishment symbol, the story of the messiah who sacrificed himself adds another dimension than that of death. According to various discussions and studies, the vertical wooden pole signifies our first connection with nature and the divine. It is our way towards our personal heaven and communion with the Creator.

The horizontal wooden pole is meant to signify our connection with the other; a sacred communion with he who looks like us. What is even more beautiful the fact that both poles are intersecting, which means that our relationship with the divine and with the other being is at some point also connected to that of the divine.

I would like to also bring your attention to the esthetic of words, which is rarely considered. Look at the word God written in Arabic.

As I looked at this beautiful word, I found an illustration that tells the story of our connection with the divine and the other since the dawn of time.

Let me break down the word for those who are not well versed in Arabic lettering.

Reading and writing Arabic is usually done from right to left, in the below table you will find an explanation of how the word is written, which will assist you in understanding my vision.

The letter in Arabic	Its English equivalent or explanation
ا	This letter is called the "alef" and is the equivalent of the letter "A". It has various pronunciations depending on the word.
ل	This letter is called "Lam" and is the equivalent of the letter "L". It has three shapes depending on its placement within a word.
ّ	This is the stress symbol or "Shaddah" and usually doubles the letter upon which it is placed.
ه	This is the "Ha'" and is the equivalent of the letter "H". It can take various shapes depending on its placement within a word.

I was jogging along my usual route thinking of how to further illustrate the relationship between humans and the divine when it hit me hard. I could clearly see with my mind's eye the word الله along with all the explanation that I needed. It was a divine revelation.

As my mind's eye looked at this symbol, the Alef reminded me of the singularity of things at the beginning of time; the union and heaven and earth that was "split as under" in the Islamic tradition. This image was also reflected in the Christian counterpart as the spirit of God hovering over the waters in Christianity and in science that saw the universe being created out of an extraordinary gravitational force that exploded. But things did not stop at this moment of creation, and with evolution and the expansion of the universe, the cooling of the planet and so on, things started to take another path, that of an exchange of energy. The emergence of man was the turning point, and with it we start the relationship between the divine and the physical dimensions. The double "L" and exemplify the beautiful give and take, while the Shaddah comes to stress the never-ending cycle. The final letter of this beautiful symbol is the "h" or ه, which I believe takes us back to the importance of uniting with the divine that is both out in the universe, but also in the beings that we are.

This second connection is very much the result of the first one. Connecting with nature brought around our higher self, and with this it has allowed us to expand, accept what is within, make room for what cannot be restricted, hence making us temples. The idea that we are connected to nature, and the idea that nature also seeks to connect with us, has allowed us to establish a deeper link with the other.

Meaningful connections seem to appear as a vital need for us to thrive and survive. Establishing random connections does not do the trick. The road to self-mastery is fraught with opportunities that look like challenges. In order to stay on track, meaningful connections play a crucial role in reminding you of your divine being's powers. They are your safety net or your personal oasis. In today's world, meaningful connections have become such a rare commodity especially with the advent social media and its illusion of happiness. It is strange how we have morphed from social Beings to social media junkies in such a short period of time. The worst part of this addiction is that it has become so ingrained in us to the extent of not only satisfying our need for attention, but also releasing hormones on the physiological level. I have seen individuals that no longer want any face-to-face interactions by fear of not being able to satisfy the other.

I cannot share the times I cry; people might think that I am asking for attention, that I am weak. I can't just post negative things on my feed.

Who put these rules? You don't have to make your life a sob story for people to pity you. No! You don't have to publish insults, or attacks or anything that might assault other beings because you would surely be shunned; however, why not turn your life into a lesson. I ask you to look at your feelings, put them before your eyes and understand them. Turn your feed into some kind of a legacy that will help others cope, understand and grow. I am not asking you to become everybody else's guru while you are trying to build yourself. Take your life one step at a time. Take your present as your anchor, release yourself and transform unfathomable feelings into your own tool. If you practice what you preach, you can become a lesson without much effort.

In the age of inconsequential and shallow attention, digital attention has become a source of dopamine for all of us, me included. I could not, at a certain period, post anything online and not peek every now and then to check my metrics. I had become hyper-vigilant because such a connection requires our human brains to be always alert just like in a flight or fight situation. This is an example of a connection with the digital world and the other through your smartphone. It is stressful. In other words, it will neither better you nor push you forward. Meaningful connections are meant to make you the best of yourself based on your belief in your being.

As we talk about establishing meaningful connections, I feel the need to cover very important aspects of our collective psyche. It is a need that is felt as part of our hardwired social composition. Respect and trust are things that no other creature, apart from humans, feels on this planet. We have been imbued with a divine sense of awe and respect that we did not understand fully at first, and still, we can hardly call ourselves scratching the surface. I am not talking about the need for approval, I am talking of full acceptance of the other and of the self. It is an understandable need since we voice opinions and concerns that shape our realities and relationships. You are the painter, musician, writer of your life and thoughts.

The COACH within

I work with lots of professionals who bring me lots of information. They are curious individuals who are always on the lookout for new ways to treat their patients. Bringing curiosity to the table means that you are open to suggestion and to ideas that might even scare you. With curiosity comes openness. You cannot be truly curious without being open. Openness is a crucial component of self-mastery, it provides one with enough lucidity and awareness to embrace things that you might have seemed too exotic, too different, or too divergent from your usual mode of thought. New ideas, new experiences, even new words might become more agreeable to you as you embrace openness.

Those who embrace openness are known to steer away from toxic routines, traditions, and clichés. When you steer away from routines, traditions, and clichés, this does not mean that you will have to throw away your healthy morning routine or any kind of ritual. I simply mean those negative stagnating cycles or vicious circles which destroy your brain and chain your Being. So, it is imperative to understand the difference between a good and bad routine. Once you open up, you allow your Being to be creative and accept others.

As you open yourself to new ideas, concepts and experiences, appreciation is *downloaded* into your *Being*. One cannot be open without appreciating the beauty of life and the beauty of diversity. I tend to link appreciation to gratitude. Acknowledging the goodness in life and having an appreciation of all things is a sure way to attract opportunities into your life. Appreciation is a part of gratitude which proves that no emotion or mode of thought can act on its own. When you vocalize your appreciation and gratitude, you will immediately be taken to the present moment; to the precious *now*. Your mindset will then shift from focusing on irritations and problems to what makes your life a beautiful one.

Compassion is obviously linked to all of the above. By practicing compassion and growing this beautiful "muscle," you will become more in tune with your surroundings and your sense of appreciation will be heightened.

> *"If you want others to be happy, practice compassion.*
> *If you want to be happy, practice compassion."*
> Dalai Lama

As you might have guessed, compassion is not a reflex, meaning that it is not automatic. You can develop your sense of compassion by being curious, aware, and empathetic. Being compassionate is an inward and an outward practice. Being self-compassionate means practicing self-kindness and being aware that nobody is perfect will transform mistakes into learning experiences.

Honesty is an idea that most people overuse. Honesty seems to have become an ambiguous blob of meanings and concepts.

Being human means being hardwired to seek connections and create meaningful relationships. When I moved to Switzerland with my parents, I felt a sense of aloofness. I was the exotic little boy who did not belong there. This is surely not any sad story for it made me who I am today, but if I am to empathize with the little boy that I was back then, the feeling that I get is one of sadness and loneliness.

Loneliness, however, should not be confused with the feeling of being alone. It is feeling left out, empty, unloved, and unwanted. This leaves the person not being able to establish any real connections especially when the feeling is further reinforced by the mind. It is normal to sometimes feel lonely, to be in need of a person to talk to, to feel part of something bigger. But feeling lonely more than twice or thrice a week is regarded as dangerous. Many of us resort to social media for approval and for social contact, but this is far from being an optimal solution.

Each and every one of us experiences loneliness in a different way, but the overarching feeling is that of a need to connect. Connection is love, mutual support and respect among others. Such connection-related attributes allow the individual or the group to have a sense of belonging and to thrive. However, it is important not to fall prey to social traps set by the mind, which are known to feed our limiting beliefs

On a more personal note, loneliness came in waves when I was leading a single life. The time in between relationships was filled with seeking approval and trying to fill my inner void. I deeply knew that this state of living was only due to insecurities, which I was not properly dealing with. Just like any other person trying to fill that void, I went out partying, met many people and was always eager to show how much of a happy person I was. In truth, I was only hiding from my emotions and from the loneliness that struck when I reached home.

Change came with my wife who is a much-grounded individual; she had the ability to guide me and act as my emotional mentor. She had awakened, thanks to her calmness, a sort of awareness by being brutally and lovingly honest with me, and this is in part of why I am living a balanced life today. Finding equilibrium allowed me to thrive on the personal, as well as on the professional level; the more people I met, the more I was able to understand myself through them. My empathy got a real good workout out dealing with so many individuals and groups.

I had overcome the mind-created loneliness by understanding myself, facing my emotions, befriending them, or at least observing them, and enjoying my own company.

The way to self-mastery might look like a rocky path or an uphill fight. The wiser path towards enlightenment and self-mastery is through lightheartedness and detachment from the mind. When I say lightheartedness, I do not mean being careless and reckless. Being lighthearted is the power to see problems as they are: situations that need to be dealt with. It is far from avoidance and closer to being objective.

Smile more, break your personal chains, laugh, accept the fact that your mind will put up a good fight, listen to your body, take situations with the seriousness they deserve without overreacting, care for others and, most importantly, care for yourself.

Kindness is crucial for humans to thrive, and despite the fact that individuals have been growing apart there have been many campaigns urging everyone to be kind to themselves and to others. The prevalent idea that we have to abide by impossible standards and live impossibly lavish online lives has frustrated people on deep levels. With the decrease of kindness and the focus on showing fake happiness, friendliness, cooperation, support and empathy, we have witnessed a dip; a major dip. Connections, which we are so much keen on establishing, hit a dead end. We have forgotten that being kind is also hardwired into our brains, which will release "happiness" hormones bolstering better and more meaningful connections. Random acts of kindness, such as leaving nice notes, sending flowers, sending simple gifts, or just saying nice things have the same impact as eating chocolate. Here's to enjoying your time minus the calories.

Going into the science of being kind, research has shown that we are the only mammals who are able to produce high volumes of oxytocin; a neurotransmitter that plays a major role in forming social bonds, feeling happy, safe and warm when meaningful connections are established. Celebrating your kindness is vital to your growth and is the actual pavement that lines your path towards self-mastery.

Kindness has a scientific side that is seldom considered by the average person. A study that was conducted on a number of individuals who were obliged to donate a number of their earnings – as part of a game – showed that mandatory donations had the same effect as being genuinely generous. In scientific terms, kindness and generosity activate a part of the brain called the ventral striatum responsible feeling pleasure.

Bringing out the best in others does not need you to be a psychologist or a specialist of any kind. If you want to bring out the best in others, you must be able to see the best in yourself first, become aware of what is limiting you. It takes the small effort of putting yourself in the other person's shoes and *observe* without judging. You might have to face people who are unable to be kind, who might be annoying or downright rude. People can be rude, annoying, and angry, but instead of taking these observations to heart and transforming them into judgments or anger, try to really see the person before you. Truly seeing means to understand that any kind of behavior is the product of a set of situations. This is easier said than done, but no athlete could do the impossible without proper training and grueling exercises. Rome was not built in a day, so train yourself to see beyond the other person's behavior. You will see that most of our negative behavior is the results of a lack of kindness. A child living in harsh conditions might go to extremes either in kindness or in meanness. A lack of kindness will result in a lifetime of feeling unworthy of love, hence leading to failed relationships, divorce, stress, lack of concentration at school and in the workplace. The list goes on as to include bullying, depression, and post-traumatic stress disorder (PTSD). I am not here to debate the importance and need to reform educational systems around the world, but teaching kindness, compassion and empathy at a young age will allow us to raise generations of beautifully shaped individuals who enjoy a deep sense of belonging, who accept others, express gratitude, have a higher self-esteem, and live a happy life simply because they *know* that they are worthy of a beautiful life.

I cannot go on talking about kindness without linking it to trust and civility, which are components of respect. With respect comes kindness, and when the two of them intertwine in our business and quotidian lives, we bring home a sense of comfort. I have talked about teaching children kindness and compassion, why? Because it will trickle down to the workplace later on as these same children grow, grow up and experience life. A heart filled with kindness and compassion can alter the course of history because everything we do is either out of love or hate. Managers at the workplace can either poison the collective feeling/consciousness or cleanse it. It all depends on how they feel, how they grew up and how they *decide* to live their lives. Of course, you are not responsible for every human being you meet, and you are not required to become an ambulant clinic but being a role model is a way to show and teach any positive attribute in a very efficient way. Here are a few things you can do to reach the best version of yourself.

- ◆ Open up to others by using the right body language with the right people
- ◆ Ask questions instead of assuming, which leads to less frustration and stress
- ◆ Listen intently, repeat the ideas you hear in your own words to check if you understood them
- ◆ Do not interrupt others
- ◆ Use a tone of voice and body language that are relaxed and relaxing

Once just one person starts a good set of actions, sooner or later, others will follow. It is the domino effect that I believe in because humans act by repetition and most of what they do is based on what they acquire during the day on a subconscious level. If humans are subconsciously exposed to kindness, their behavior will eventually change. Kindness, respect and civility are contagious. We tend to forget how strong their impact can be on groups if at least one person bases his or her actions on those three pillars. Once the trend catches momentum, members of that group or family will be able to share information, become more productive and establish a healthier and more productive lifestyle away from stress and its repercussions.

You will always meet people who seem to be off, or a little tough to say the least. I was so in the early years when was starting to establish my business. I was so eager to prove myself to everyone – to my father in particular. I was addicted to success, and being an entrepreneur, manager, owner, leader and employer had led me to be a little bit rough with my employees and the people closest to me. Even my wife got a piece of my mind at some point, but as I had already mentioned, she was brutally honest and grounded, and was able to lead me out of my tunnel vision of what life should or should not be. In other words, she showed me how I was acting with others, hence allowing me to experience my own behavior reflected back at me.

You can act as such with any person you meet; you can be the soul that pulls out another from a gaping abyss by the sole power of kindness and honesty. It is a tough game to play, but *impossible* is merely an illusion set by our limiting beliefs. These in turn are also illusions that are picked up by our brains as reality.

By being kind, you start understanding a very critical concept, that of co-dependence and the beautiful connection that comes with it. I had already mentioned that we all seek some sort of meaningful connection. Connecting with others through kindness and unconditional love secures an understanding that we all depend on each other at some point. You get to see that you influence your entourage. This might blow the egos of some, and it did with me. I had started thinking that it was all about how much control I can exert over others that made me successful. But my wife too, and I am fortunate to have met her, pointed out that there was more to my business life than assuming control based on my egoic needs. The insecurities I was battling had flared hence alienating myself from others.

Upon allowing the mind to express itself, illusion, and reality merge into one. We tend to forget that we are the key to our kingdoms. Some of you might be thinking that the image your minds create is truth. But have you proof of that? Have you proof that your mind has not infected your ego and hence your self-talk – conscious or not – is affecting your daily life?

When my wife pointed out that I was placing myself at the center of the universe. My mind's reaction was one of denial;

a normal reaction, or better called a defense mechanism. Survival is hardwired into every cell of our bodies, minds, and Beings. But then, it struck me as true. I was in fact acting as though I, as a human Being, was not connected to others and that my decisions were only my own.

Of course, your decisions are your own! I mean,
what would anybody else have to do with your decisions?

When you lead companies, employees, a small group of people, your family or dealing with just a couple of friends, whatever you decide will have a ripple effect. Basing your decisions on awareness and kindness, which are core components of unconditional love, will have the desired effect immediately and in the long run. I was able to understand that when I got to interact with my employees and get insight into their needs. I was able to wear their shoes for a while and trace the impact of my decisions. I was able to see how we are all co-dependent.

What about those who poison the workplace? I don't know how to describe them, but I guess the expression "bad apples" might do the trick. What are we supposed to do with them? How do we deal with such people and negative situations?

This is a very relevant question. In fact, the answer will always be to focus and be kind to yourself. Others might have bad energy surrounding them. Some might call it an aura; I call it their own canvas. This canvas is painted using their limiting beliefs, insecurities, fears and so on, and only affects them. You might tell me that they might hurt others' feelings, snitch on some, and cause people to lose their jobs. I totally agree with you, but why not go with the flow of things – as opposed to resisting – and be kind to those people. It might seem strange at first and very difficult to achieve because our thought patterns immediately shift towards disliking the people who dislike us. But I have learned that just like any other network, our brains emit signals. The more we think that we dislike that person or hate the other, the more they will dip into the darkness that they have created around them. So, instead positively influencing your relationship, those negative feelings will only lead you to a self-fulfilling prophecy. Such thoughts are the weeds in your garden. Pull them out. Remember, your mind and brain will grow whatever you sow into them. Hatred will grow into your personal hell. Love will blossom into your personal heaven.

Your decisions will affect you and everyone around you (again co-dependence), thus negativity will put you in a dark corner. Despite the immediate satisfaction that shouting at someone or slamming a door, or breaking something might bring in terms of catharsis, the repercussions that ensue will most likely not be in your favor. Practicing mindfulness will expand the power of your conscious mind, which usually relies on preset programs downloaded during our first seven years.

Humans have the ability to become mindful. This means that we have the ability to read our own minds in a sort of routine check. Self-mastery will become a closer to your grasp once you understand that all that you see around you is the work of your mind. All that you struggle with, all the issues you face have been downloaded into your system by years of apprenticeship with your parents who provided you with all they know (be it good or bad), friends, acquaintances, teachers, university professors, etc.

Opening your eyes to the truth is a beautiful, but slightly shocking process; you will become aware of how every little thing in your life, from choosing your meal to your relationships, is the result of our taming as children. As you enter the light, reaching your true self will become a faster process. Breaking the taming cycle will require some serious work. Positive self-talk is one of them as choosing your words will have to be flawless. You will be required to understand the inner workings of your mind, its defense mechanisms, its wants and needs. You will have to understand what your Being wants, receive its messages and allow its energy to course through you. Once you start truly listening, you will know the words to use.

I have started positive and healthy self-talk years ago. It seemed simple and complex at the same time. I felt the power emanating from my words, but I could seldom know how to properly wield them. The challenge here is to know exactly what works for you. It took me a good deal of research to understand that the most widely used expressions, which seem harmless, can sabotage your day. Using the wrong words will lead you to living in anxiety, stress, and self-doubt among other feelings. I had to recognize negative thought patterns, order myself to stop and halt the downward spiral. After stopping myself, I had to face my own limiting beliefs and doubts. I had to put my thoughts under the magnifying glass and sort out what is helpful from what is not.

On Friends & Empathy

You, the social human Being, are part of the collective consciousness, part of the psychic environment that surrounds you. Empathy is the element that purifies that collective consciousness from the pollution that emanates from many, be it conscious or not. You will find that various individuals and even whole populations practice self-deprecation on a regular basis. This is the poison you need to avoid and/or reverse starting with yourself and then allowing that energy to ripple out to others. Empathy is the ability to mirror other people's feelings and emotions. We have evolved so much on the emotional level that the meaningful connections that we establish with our analogues have extended their reach into our cores. This means that should someone you care about feel anxious and their heartrate spike, you would experience almost the same exact symptoms. Our bodies partially simulate other people's experiences from facial expressions to heart rate and even hormone release. Aside from having innate responses, empathy can be voluntary. This special skill is also referred to as cognitive empathy. Practicing empathy means making sense of what the other is experiencing. Voluntary and involuntary empathy are complementary, and act on two intertwining levels: the basic, primeval, and involuntary decision-making reflex, and the higher-order perceptual pathways. The latter level allows us to identify the incredibly diverse and nuanced array of emotional signals.

It is crucial that you feel with others, it is not enough to enjoy good times with your friends and then once things become a little somber, to take flight. Empathy is not exposing yourself to the emotions of others. Being empathetic means that you can feel what the other is feeling, understand the process that had led them to this particular point and know how to guide them out of that foggy situation. This also applies to positive emotions whereby you can amplify and support the person before you. Both situations should never drain you, instead, you will feel an overwhelming sensation of humanity and your divine Being will bathe in the strength and knowledge that you give and gain from empathetic interactions.

Being empathic has its benefits and has clear signs. People who are more empathic are more socially successful. They are seen as more appealing and competent since they know the underlying dynamics of the various situations they deal with.

Their relationships tend to be higher in quality, more supportive and satisfying. They are also happier and healthier. Patients are more satisfied and do better under the care of empathic medical providers, just like students fare better under the supervision of empathetic teachers.

There are so many ways to show that you are empathizing with others. The first and foremost is body language, which allows you to display interest. You can mindfully nod, maintain eye contact, touch the other person whenever it feels right and appropriate and mirroring their body language and gestures. By showing your interest through body language, you will be dampening much of their negative emotions. I repeat, you will not be carrying them on your back. You will not be switching psychological and ancestral loads. You will be merely showing them that they have the strength to deal with their situations. You are not asked to plan your next answer, and you are not asked to solve their problems. The simple act of being empathetic is powerful enough on its own because it relies on sharing experiences and being humane. Empathy is a vital part of unconditional love and the root that makes all connections meaningful. Without empathy, we would be akin to robots; detached and cold. Empathy is that one mental communication that we must cherish as it does not really require words. Your mere presence will have an immediate impact.

Humans need empathy to survive and thrive in a world where individualism is taking center stage. But what about compassion? Where does it stand here?

Compassion is what we call 'empathetic concern' or 'active empathy.' This particular type of empathy goes beyond the realm of sensing and focusing your thoughts on the other person's feelings and emotions. Compassion is thinking of ways to help solve the issue at hand. Compassion is the feeling we have when we sense another person's suffering and feel a strong desire to help alleviate that suffering. When you practice compassion, your body will react to a call for help. These situations will activate certain circuits in your brain that suppresses response to pain, activate the kindness/pleasure feeling, as well as the urge to care and nurture. Many studies have labeled responses triggered by compassion as an innate trait, and have shown that compassionate individuals enjoy better health, stronger social interactions, better relationship quality and a better general sense of happiness.

Is compassion innate or acquired?

Compassion can be innate, but this does not mean that you cannot develop it as you go. You can train yourself to practice compassion and trigger the same positive responses. Neuroscience has shown that the human brain is hardwired to experience other people's emotions and sensations, which means that whether you are born with it or not, you can practice and fire-up those neurons, strengthening them and making those connections stronger and more efficient.

Compassion is so important that it has been set as the most significant principle of medical ethics, especially when it comes to the activation of the nurturing and caretaking parts of the brain. This means that we can actively bypass pain and fear, which makes this superpower a necessity in the healthcare and medical field. I believe that compassion and empathy make up the foundation of any professional field since employees who rate their workplaces as more compassionate, also report more frequent positive emotional experiences, greater commitment to their organization and perform their tasks with a higher success rate.

How do we inject more compassion into our work lives?

- ◆ Reflecting on those easy-to-feel moments of compassion, like when we spontaneously comfort close friends or family members
- ◆ Directing those kinds of feelings towards someone at work
- ◆ Reflecting on the fact that every person at work, like ourselves, was once a small child who deserved love and protection.

As I have mentioned before, I went through the classic "tough love" phase. I don't know if I can actually call it tough love or only being business-oriented, but I felt I needed to push everyone around me to be productive, move everything at my pace and manage my home the way I saw fit. This obviously did not work. My employees were unhappy with their workplace being negatively charged. My wife, who was aware of what I was going through, did not want me to go down that road. It took me some time to understand that their opinions really mattered. I was business-oriented, and everything fell into the business category for me. I lived in the absence of compassion and empathy. I lived a life in the absence of love. Looking back at that period, I can still feel how distant I was, I felt as though I was living my life outside my body, experiencing things as though my body was a puppet. I was a robot performing its duties and I was witnessing it all through a glass wall. The glass wall is your mind separating your Being from your body in such a way as to take up the whole space within the body. Once you are pushed outside the body, it will be easy for the mind to sabotage your relationships, decrease your productivity, cause anxiety and depression and bring about a feeling of hopelessness.

Once my wife pointed out that I was going out of control, I sought to break this cycle by doing things that brought my Being happiness and recharge its power: I read out loud, slept early, practiced meditation, focused on controlling my reactions, sought the presence of my friends and family, and finally relied on music and breathing exercises as a means to purify my Being. This collection of seemingly simple lifestyle choices helped me find the power and put my Being where it belongs.

So, a life without love, empathy
and compassion is a life of conflict and stress.

This is extremely accurate. A person living a life away from love, empathy and compassion will only attract the like. A life lacking in humane aspects and feelings will lead to failed relationships and professional life.

Life is best lived in love, it is what can change the world. Self-mastery is changing the world; it is change that starts from within and ripples out. Changing the world is not something that we dream of. Changing the world requires the understanding that whatever we see is nothing short of calculated stunts. It is acquiring the awareness that we cannot move forward if we keep looking back.

To cleanse the collective consciousness, and alter your own reality, start by making peace with yourself, mastering your emotions, mastering yourself, and then move on to the outside world.

Here a few simple steps that will guide you closer to that coveted awareness:

♦ Be considerate and kind in your everyday acts.

♦ Use polite language and kind speech.

♦ Genuinely compliment others to create goodwill.

♦ Try to make light of conflict-laden moments without underestimating their potential importance.

♦ Be modest in your speech and be modest in how you comport yourself. It's actually a way in which people respect and trust you more.

♦ Apologize; hold yourself accountable - simply and genuinely saying sorry immediately upon making a mistake.

♦ Be forgiving, recognize that people are human, that they make mistakes and that they can create conflict because of what they carry around in terms of stress and psychological luggage. Forgiveness is reducing your punitive tendency hence pulling away from the "an eye for an eye" justice. Override negativity with forgiveness. Remember, true positive feelings ripple out stronger than their negative counterparts.

Once you start practicing the points above, and I am sure you will be able to find steps that work for you too, you will start understanding the major concept of forgiveness. It has been preached all over the world.

SPIRITUAL HEALTH

I f you read any of the ancient hymns, stories, and myths, you'll find that they were all written with out-worldly wisdom; you might feel that they are abstract and ambiguous. As a part of my attempts at reaching enlightenment and understanding, I have studied as much as I can about religions from Christianity to Buddhism to Islam, which despite it being my own religion, had always had a certain concealed side that attracted me. Having all that knowledge so readily available feels like carrying a large bag of gold on your back, while remaining oblivious to its content. There is no weight when approaching religious text but thanks to my insight into the various spiritual teachings many things have come to make more sense. What I have reached did not in any way oppose or hinder my pragmatic mode of thinking, on the contrary, it was full of common sense and straightforward links to everything that I had heard and read about. The law of attraction, manifestation, consistency, constancy, acceptance, and unconditional love were integral parts of those religions and spiritual teachings, old and new.

I have read the Holy Bible – Old and New Testaments – only to find hints leading us to living in peace with ourselves and with the other. Every expression, anecdote and verse are so rich with techniques to bring you to the present moment and enjoy your pure self, body, and soul. I have read the Holy Quran, only to find the same exact path painted with a different brush. It all goes back to love; loving yourself, loving others, loving the universe, and ultimately *knowing* that you are part of a cycle just like water. And just like water you are asked not to resist. Once you let go of the border and go to the deep end, you'll understand that you can float and feel light, only fear and doubt can be your downfall if you allow them in.

This also applies to the Buddhist teachings that I have come in contact with. It is all the same everywhere, and our human eyes and man-made religious boundaries have not only concealed their true meanings and life-changing potential, but also destroyed the bond that connects humans to each other. We are creatures with built-in frequency generators; our brains are the most powerful means of reaching out to others, feeling others, and spreading love. Haven't you at some point had the image of a person pop up in your mind only to stumble across them on that same day? Such instances are the simplest forms of connection that we can establish with others. Imagine the power that we could wield if we practiced mindfulness, active and passive meditation as well as a host of other techniques that will bolster the power of your inner Being.

I cannot claim to be religious. I respect my religion, but I have liberated myself with that which looks like is fabricated by the human mind. Fabricated things or lies, originate in the mind, dig their roots deep and brainwash you into believing in a sense of self that is a shadow of you. Look for the *Truth*, it is not that hard to find, it is the only thing that exists and is autonomous. The lies you are experiencing, and that look so real, are the leeches stuck on your back; you can't see them, but you can feel them sucking the life out of you. You can be a believer in God; you can choose to believe in another entity that might not be given a name, you are free to choose, but you are required to read and *feel* the word and extract the energy behind it.

The Lost and Found; Soul

I have been haunted for so long with the concept of soul that it has become something of a legend to my brain. After years and years of building a life on the physical plane, working to establish myself as an entrepreneur and businessman, I was faced with an internal question, that of understanding what keeps the soul going. It seems like only yesterday that I had started looking for a meaning of soul and found that we have been only using it so much that, just like the word god, it had become so diluted. Human beings have so many expressions using the word soul that describe anything and everything. It is quite interesting because to my mind's eye, at this very moment, I can feel the energy behind those idiomatic expressions, yet at the time, it was very difficult. It wasn't long after my third child got really sick and my business life on a really rocky road that my soul was struck by lightning, if I may depict it that way. It felt as though things were not in my favor. In fact, I felt my very core crumble, and with that I felt that I had let my soul down, then came my heart attack.

It is easy to talk of soul as if it is something that we cannot see. It is hard to talk of soul as if something we understand. Being Lebanese, means that I was fortunate enough to learn the Arabic language. I had noted something quite interesting as I was thinking of the concept of soul. I found that Arabic speaking populations use the word نفس pronounced Nafs and Nafas, to mention soul and breathe respectively. The immeasurable power behind the word نفس in the Arabic language can only be explained by the soulfulness of that language. What makes this language even more attractive is the fact that it makes breath and soul seem like one and the same. Case in point, many of the endearing expressions that we use include calling our loved ones as "my soul" or "my life." This also applies to physical pain which is described to pain the soul when it is very acute. The Arabic language is full of those little gems that reflect its link to universal power.

It would be quite tempting to think that we can make the soul palpable, a thing or possession of some sort. But the quality of soul is not something that we can trade; it is not a commodity that we can scrutinize, exchange, alter and paint the way we like. Soul is not simply the belief that it is the part of us that remains after death. It is not something so human that it resembles our physical form and simply animates our bodies. True, Christianity and Islam, for instance, believe that the soul will mirror the host body in form, or at least, in the case of saints, prophets and celestial beings, appear in specific shapes and personas to serve a certain aim or reach an objective. But we tend to forget that soul also comes in other forms of the act creation. Soul is in color, music, speech, and movement; art is the embodiment of soul and soul is life. It is the very expression of the beauty that resides within. I have been using the expression "a beautiful soul" for so long that it had lost its true meaning. But if I am to think of it, I would certainly use it with people whose inner beauty is reflected outwardly. A beautiful soul is a kind and giving soul that lives and flourishes through compassion and empathy.

The most common way to approach the idea of soul is through transforming our physical bodies into temples of love and creation to this Being. But let me ask you a question, aren't we still limiting soul the way we limit God with our human understanding of nature and what lies beyond?

I have thought so many times of why we fear God. Why we are not able to regard Him as an entity that is transcendent and that lives in every one of our cells. I wonder why we have not been able to see that we live within the being we call God in a kind of cycle that is an infinite loop of unconditional love. This brings me back to the idea that we cannot be part of this universe yet dissociated from it. Soul is God and God is soul, and understanding it is beyond our physical nature.

The soul is who you truly are at the core. The soul is the Being that I have spoken about throughout this book. Being or soul, this divine entity is the largest part of you; neither your body, nor your mind can take up as much spacetime as your soul, Nafs or Being. The soul is larger than life; it is what animates your thoughts, brings about inspiration; that divine message coming from all around you. With inspiration come passion and a very intimate exchange between your soul and the life force that moves the world.

We talk of soulmates, soul food, etc... Yet, we do not ponder the words we use. The power of our souls comes through the use of words, which is why we all have to know what each word truly means. I have spoken of the power of thought, the power of their frequencies, and the power of the Being inside and their overarching connection, so try to keep in mind that all things in this world are interconnected, hence blessed, or cursed by those words.

I agree with your view that we are connected, I can feel others, but is it true that we can read minds? Where is the privacy in that?

I was conducting some research the other day, and the below meme grabbed my attention.

It was apparent that the person behind the meme had some kind of awareness, and willingly or unwillingly saw through our fear. We can develop psychic abilities and become a network of brains. However, it is up to you to share the thoughts you want to share. It is very much like allowing an app on your smartphone to access all photos or simply one of your folders. All I can say in light of such revelation is: Trust the process and enjoy it because you are in control. If you are doubtful and fearful of the power you have, then it will never be accessible to you, which takes us back again to proper and *impeccable* self-talk, add to that fully trusting your Being.

Fear is like a leash; it is used on us ever since we are born into this world, and we tend to use it on others for whatever purpose or agenda we have. Don Miguel Ruiz called this domestication in The Four Agreements, others sugarcoated it and called it being reared or disciplined. But it is all based on fear. This is based on the anticipation that something bad will happen; hence studies have been conducted on the errors and ailments of the mind, rather than on the goodness and amazing potential of our existence. We have not only grown to fear ourselves, but fear *fear* itself.

How do I fight fear?

Fear cannot be fought; it must simply not be fed; that is the secret to success and the road to salvation. Haven't you ever noticed how numerous people who hold no degree and had no formal education have come to lead superbly successful lives? They do not give their fear anything to grow; they do not allow it to control their beings. In other words, such people were able to look at success, accept it as a normal part of their lives and *claim* it. Such people were able to accept that life has its downs too, but they did some long-term planning while keeping their objectives in mind. Fear can be morphed and remodeled to serve us in our day-to-day survival efforts.

Can't I just kill my fear? Wouldn't that help me live a happier life? Wouldn't that make me more courageous and assertive?

Without your biceps, your triceps would not have any real role. Without light there would be no dark. Living is an art; an act of equilibrium where you have to keep the balance. If you kill your fear, you would make rash decisions, be reckless, impulsive in ways so extreme to the extent of becoming pathological. The total absence of fear is the unhealthy alternative to being aware of it and understanding that it stems from within us and from our education. What I would like to point out that once you befriend your fear, it morphs into a higher awareness and opens your eyes to the fact that challenges are possibilities and opportunities. Stress can be turned into excitement, fear can be turned into strength, you have to take the reins and lead that carriage to the destination you wish to reach.

Consciousness is Silence

What is consciousness? Still, nobody has a definitive answer! The lack of insight into this particular aspect of our human constitution has remained hidden for eons and will most probably remain so. But I can share my own views and analysis, and I do believe that whatever we consider and set under the umbrella of "consciousness," may be the perfect answer.

I tend to see consciousness as that timeless, unconditional power bestowed on us by the creator. We were made to handle this power in the best way possible and all the chemicals that course through our systems, all those hormones, electrical signals and beautiful breaths are some of the tools that can bolster our development as Beings. I have read in many publications that we are the greatest magnets in existence and that we possess powers beyond imagining. This is true! We are as powerful as the sun itself; we withhold auras that shine but cannot be seen by our physiologically ignorant eyes.

Throughout history, there have been so many instances of people who have made miracles during their lifetimes. Monks, nuns, sheikhs, yogis, etc. call them what you want. They are people who understood the concept of not being their minds. By dissociating themselves from the negative loop that feeds that entity, they entered enlightenment, but I would better call it ultimate consciousness.

I believe that consciousness is made of two elements: unconsciousness and awareness. The unconscious part, in its classical definition, is the seat of all things unseen and divine. The unconscious is where the ultimate knowledge was pre-stored and encrypted only to be decrypted by awareness. I do not seek to debate what consciousness is, but to attempt to understand its functionalities and assist in tapping into your full potential. When I say that awareness decrypts unconscious information, I mean that it is the key and the "eye-opener" and our medium to scrutinize our behavior, emotions and feeling, and finally understand their causes. It is like grabbing that slippery little toad and dissecting it. Things might get messy, but the effort is worth it. Various specialists have created techniques to allow you to understand this part of human existence, but their endeavors have been majorly pragmatic, focusing on the mind and its issues, rather than on its strengths. Such studies have shown great promise, but why settle for great promise and hopes while we can have something close to ultimate success.

What makes consciousness a versatile tool is the fact that it is flexible. It can stretch to infinity and can implode just like a supernova, leaving nothing but a little weakling. Flexibility does not come by overnight; it is a beautiful process of acceptance. It is seeing your being's depth and correcting your view of the world.

Imagine consciousness as your body. Flexibility is one of the most important attributes for great overall wellbeing. Imagine that you are exercising, lifting weights, and then immediately leaving the gym. Sooner or later, you would suffer an imbalance. Change and our reaction to change are double-edged swords. You are required to focus on wanting and accepting change. Change is already a difficult thing to deal with. Yet, everybody wants to change something, everybody wants to change the world, make an impact, change their appearance, and alter the way they speak, walk, and move.

Change is a coveted yet feared process; however, the seed of change can be found within each one of us as we are equipped to instigate change, negative be it or positive; it is a matter of awareness and taking the right decision. In order for change to take place, especially positive change, you are asked to do your best in implementing a very important point that I have already mentioned. You are asked to relinquish all that society has tattooed unto your brain with virtual ink. Think in terms of unconditional energy. Think that divine energy will never come to you and poke you in the eye, asking you to retract your demand because it is "not good" or "too exaggerated."

The divine is not human and is beyond our thinking, therefore judgment, even in its religious sense, does not stand in the face of God and in the face of our consciousness that seeks change. Let us say that, for instance, you wish for fame and fortune, yet your parents have only been showing you the bad side of being famous and rich, you will most certainly awaken the impostor in you and sabotage all your plans.

Being skeptical in healthy doses is the one thing that you should focus on. You need to look at your own thoughts and contest their origins. Learn to ask yourself whether your feelings and decisions make sense to your Being, not only to your mind. Your mind will only tell that this or that thing is acceptable, unacceptable, beautiful, ugly, etc. but is there is proof to back those claims?

Be the consciousness behind your actions, reactions, feelings, emotions, and decisions; be the entity that gives pure and powerful intent. Instead of being impulsive, breathe and allow your awareness to put everything in the light. There might be conflicts within us regarding that one topic or the other.

But what if there was not one answer. What if everything in this world is perfect in both its poles, including everything in between? Becoming a fully ready, activated, well-trained and open consciousness is one of the most important steps towards reaching self-mastery. In fact, mastering your consciousness, training it, knowing its states, and moving from one state to another, at will, is crucial to acquiring the fundamentals of the art of self-mastery and to the mastery of your reality.

The Good Place

The Good Place is an American fantasy comedy that takes place in the afterlife, and places four humans in morally distressing situation alongside some nicely comic action scenes.

This show's very title is the place we all seek, eternal peace and bliss. We all want to reach that good place and become masters of the self, masters of the universal energy. As I watched the show, I was struck by the way things unfold. It is definitely a beautiful series that can serve you well; it can get you thinking about even the smallest actions you take and how they can affect you and others. On the personal level, it got me thinking of whether my actions will lead me to my destination. I even wondered whether I was fair and supportive of my *Being*. Furthermore, I was able to clearly see the mind v/s *Being* clashing.

Introducing Janet: Janet is a female humanoid being that has access to all information in the universe. She… it – as she prefers not being assigned to a specific gender – is akin to the Google Assistant, Siri, Alexa or Cortana, but in a much more complex way. I found as I went through the short episodes that she represents the dichotomy of the *being* and the mind. The creator of the show Michael Schur made Janet one of the most powerful celestial beings in the universe, but also assigned a button to that being that renders it powerless; Schur called it marbleization and it only required the use of a pin.

Imagine that this button is the mind's weapon or the mind itself if you want to, and it disconnects you from your universal knowledge. It might seem like a tiny button, but it can morph you into a tiny little marble ball as per the writer.

What is beautiful about this character is that it is the truth. It does not ascribe itself to any small category other than being herself; "not a girl" being one of her statements. Yet, "Janets" – I have used this proper name in the plural as there are many versions of that being in the series – are prone to glitching as are humans prone to making mistakes. We, humans, dislike, even despise making mistakes to the extent of fearing them. Fear grips us by the throat and limits our ability to properly function; we then start looking at worst case scenarios, expecting the worst and creating self-fulfilling prophecies. We always tend to forget that through those little (or sometimes big) annoyances we can find the gate (and the key) to a higher self; one that is acquiring knowledge from the world around us in such a way as to append all that new data to our everlasting consciousness. The trickster inside is a shapeshifter, it constantly strives to make us feel smaller, but it can also appeal to our emotions through guilt and fear.

Case in point, in that same series, a Janet is hardwired to start appealing to your "better self", fervently pleading not to end its life. Despite the fact that Janets cannot die, a big red button that halts its functioning triggers desperation, fear, and is akin to our dissociation process from the mind. The mind is master of emotional manipulation, and as any of The Place Characters tries to approach the button, Janet will start using its arsenal in strategic ways in order not to be rebooted. Little did it know that with every reboot, it will get stronger as a *Being*. Death or termination flair up our self-pity, which we ought to let pass.

"If there were an answer, I could give you to how the universe works, it wouldn't be special. It would just be machinery fulfilling its cosmic design. It would just be a big, dumb food processor. But since nothing seems to make sense, when you find something or someone that does, it's euphoria." Janet to Eleanor

The mind will fear your ability to access universal information and it will fear its own death. So instead of feeling its fear, pay attention to attention and focus all your intent and life force on the idea that you are beyond what you think you are.

We are more than we think we are.

If we are to think of life and how we interact with our environment, we find that it is all found in frequencies. Everything around us is frequency, from light, to colors, to sounds and so on. We interact with frequencies, and we allow them to shape our view of the world. Everything around us vibrates at various frequencies; it is a natural law that reigns over all things and Beings. Have you ever given a thought to what makes things solid, liquid or gas? It is specific vibrations that shape the world around us. Things that are solid vibrate at a certain frequency that allows them to keep their shape and size, liquids vibrate at different ones that allow them to slide and run along surfaces, gases have another set of frequencies that makes them light and free. Everything about us and the environment around us is ruled by the law of frequency. Why not learn from the way water changes and shifts from liquid to solid to gas? Why not get inspired by the beautiful natural cycles that surround us?

We interact with frequencies; we catch them, reflect them, love them, hate them, accept them, and block them (or try to at best we can). Whenever we hear a nice song, we turn up the volume and vibrate to that frequency; we smile, laugh, feel sad, cry, feel energetic and so on. Whenever works and noise start early in the morning right outside our houses, the monotonous sound of machines, the roar of trucks and the shouts of workers trying to get things done might make us cringe and feel upset; they feel disruptive and annoying, and we vibrate along with these same frequencies while trying to block them and cleanse our systems of these little annoyances. If we can be so affected by what one sense can provide us with, I can assure you that our five senses conceal the greatest potential for shaping your reality.

If I am to use language to describe the greatness that we conceal inside, it would most certainly not do it justice; it would be like trying to catch light inside a jar. But, in my attempt at understanding the potential of the being, I have come across the concept of letting go of our mind-shaped human identity. Once we dissociate with the mind, it becomes easier for us to let go of all the imagery that has been used to depict us. We become just what and who we are, and each one of us would be able to answer the "who are you?" question with the simple and ultimate truth; "I am."

It is quite easy for us to allow to become blunt the tools we use to ward off the attacks of the mind, but if we keep our eyes fixed on the image that we are made of infinitely smaller things, and that these seemingly invisible things support our bodies, it becomes easier for us to face those blows with smart dodges and smarter grabs. Just like anything else in this universe we are made of matter, and matter is made of molecules. Molecules are made of atoms and the latter are made of protons, neutrons and electrons, and as we try to go deeper into that interstellar personal space, we find that what has been believed to be the smallest of things are actually made of smaller entities called quarks. Thinking of these things can make you feel small or maybe big. All you have to know is the fact that you can be whoever and whatever you want; you can become the whole universe since it is within you. Everything that I have stated right here is made of energy; things carry energy and share energy; they are interconnected just like the internet connects everything around you. This energy holds your body together, holds your house together and supports your reality.

If God has created us in His own image and we are God and God is within us, then the process applies to us upon our personal act of creation. I believe that you are familiar with the concept of polarity; the negative and the positive, solid and gas (although this one has an intermediary stage in between), light and dark, life and death, etc. This polarity could be noted in all religious and spiritual books and were meant to give meaning to the world.

Such views were taken in a very simplistic manner, but they hold much more than the eye can see. Polarity is something that we control as Gods. We are the intent and the force behind the change while being that change *per se*. With the power of creation bestowed upon us, we have created everything we use so far, and akin to our bodies, these creations grow old and degrade over time; however, at the core of these things is a sort of polarity and a binary system that swings between light and dark, negative and positive, quiet and explosion. Take our cars of instance, everything about them has two polar opposites and runs on a binary system; from the headlights that cast out long rays, to the computers that manage every task these vehicles require to stay up and running. Amid all this swinging, amid all these amazing changes, we emerge as the force that oversees it all; we switch our cars, lights, electrical appliances on and off, we push the doors open and we shut them, we create motion and motion is us and within us. We interact with frequencies in a direct way and can influence those frequencies too. If I am that force, then my reality is of my own making, and I can manage it.

There were many myths across the centuries that sought to point us humans in the right directions, stories, and fables of grand adventures so inspiring that the reader would get a taste of divine power. Hercules, Jason, Thor, Frey, Freya, Zeus, Apollo… all these were not only gods in the classical meaning, they were men! Just like me and you. They understood strife, jealousy, love, hate, kinship. They knew that once they influenced reality, reality will shift according to their whims. Those same gods and demi-gods were given titles according to natural phenomena, which are also frequencies and polar opposites. Speaking of frequencies, the humming or Om traditions in yoga, mirrors that of Christians bells and the Islamic calls for prayer. The *Om* sound, which is made out of three syllables (a, u and m), is said to represent the whole universe and the union of the mind, body and spirit. Church bells have their own frequency and usually start with a primary note that decays slowly followed by a number of subharmonic notes that sound like and are called the hum. In the Islamic tradition, the way calls for prayers are broadcast also relies on the nasal resonance, which compliments the *Om* and the sound of church bells. Such rooted traditions only prove that we are frequency, that frequency affects us and that we can affect frequency by being part of the cycle. Furthermore, the Om,

205

the bells, and the calls for prayer are reminders and supporters to bring our mind back to the present moment.

There was always a role for frequencies in the universe and we innately know this since we are emitters and receptors of those frequencies. When frequencies die out, we create new ones, mix old and new patterns, create instruments, and become instruments ourselves through the practice of singing and chanting. We are creators and we are the ultimate frequency. If we perceive light, sound, taste, smell, and touch, we are also very well equipped to perceive thoughts, which are frequencies as well and the foundation of our reality. By controlling and altering our thoughts, we can create and change reality by influencing our environment. From a scientific point of view, our thoughts are pulses of electricity that surge through our brains and our movements are also surges of electricity that light up our neural system, and just like electricity in wires hums at a certain frequency through walls, our thoughts pass through the cranium reaching everything and everyone around us. In short, we personally ripple out affecting our reality. Why would a person with a few good moves transform an otherwise dull party into a dance fest? Why would invitees who were shy to come to the dance floor suddenly want to dance and have a good time? Truth be told that same person has allowed his energy to ripple out to those around him and was generous enough to jump into the deep end.

This is just another simple example of how humans can be generators of massive changes around them. The belief that you are a good singer, dancer, speaker, lover, father, mother, child, aunt, uncle, and businessman and so on will amplify your frequencies and others will surely perceive them on a conscious or unconscious level. Historically speaking, there have been many individuals who made use of that energy and that knowledge for good purposes, while others did the exact opposite. Little did the latter know that despite the universe unconditionally providing the energy, the fundamental power that rules over the universe is that of pure love, any other frequency can spike, shine, but will burn out quite quickly.

Being a positive anchor and being in sync with the universe has been proven over and over again to alter whole communities on various levels. Going back to the dancer example above, I would like to draw your attention to that person's attention, to the awareness that there is a need for something to lift everyone else. This requires courage and just like all other things in life, courage has a frequency and it considered like an opportunity-creator or a door opener; once you step into the circle with courage, everything else will follow your lead, everyone else will be affected by your energy and things will move forward. Courage allows you to amplify your frequencies as opposed to shrinking them; being bold and believing in the power that is given to you will allow you to lift people around you, not just those in your direct environment, but also those in your area. Frequencies do not choose to stop at a certain place or when they reach a certain person.

I have developed an interest in quantum mechanics as of late, and the most important thing that got stuck in my mind is the fact that things have been proven to be able to be present in two places at the same time. It was that one experiment, which involved a low frequency laser, and by low frequency I mean that it can be tuned down to release only one proton at a time. Right before that screen a piece of cardboard with two holes was placed as an obstacle. As the laser hit the piece of cardboard right in the middle, the receptor behind it recorded random photon activity, which, according to the scientists conducting the experiment, proved that photons can be present in two places at the same time. In other words, reality as we see it, and frequencies as we perceive them, are mirrored elsewhere. This goes in parallel with the concept of alternate realities and parallel universes.

Many writers have pointed out the fact that we are the most powerful transmitters in the universe thanks to our awareness and our ability to shift our modes of thought. To prove this point, a bird might feel hungry, it will go find food, but it cannot manifest more than that. Yet, what we can learn from animals is that they just are and are content with their reality. We might not be aware of what is happening within their brains, but we do know that animals and insects are beings that only know what they are and nothing more. A predator is a predator and nothing else. It will not react violently if you insult it. It will not lick your hand if you go sing to it. It just is and will kill to feed. We humans live and experience a scale of emotions and feeling ranging from the darkness of guilt to enlightenment. That spectrum was not established haphazardly. In fact, it is based on the idea that humans either accept themselves and their environment, or just downright hate it. No one can live in limbo.

Resilience: Mastering Life

Soul is a dimension of existence that goes beyond space and time. Soul provides us with the ability to maintain a moment-by-moment awareness of our thoughts, feelings, bodily sensations, and surrounding environment through a gentle, nurturing lens. Why a lens? Because our bodies are not yet primed to handle the raw power of the soul. We are but vessels of that power of love and it is only through awareness and mindfulness that we can keep our bodies aligned with our souls. With being fully aligned with the soul and universe, the power that we claim can radiate from within and shine through to others. Without this alignment, conflict would arise, and a war between the soul's infinite knowledge and the body's boundaries erupts, allowing the mind to restrict the soul or Being. We are living in the physical world, and the power of the mind only grows when we give it leeway to act, it is then that many of our issues will be set ablaze, many of our thoughts turn into judgment and many of our emotions and feelings feel like oozing and bubbling toxic swamps. Take the time to show your Being or soul the love it deserves, and it will return it a thousand folds.

Keeping our bodies and souls aligned builds up our resilience to external and internal attacks. The quietude that ensues allows for mindfulness to expand, for our consciousness to expand, thus regulating our emotions and making stress and problems nothing but passing situations that we regard with objectivity. Should we allow our minds to take over, or should our autopilot always be engaged, negative emotional experiences, anxiety, depressive symptoms, burnout, and workplace withdrawal behaviors will always plague our existence.

When I talk about resilience, I feel the urge to talk about the power of authenticity. Mindfulness is associated with another factor of resilience, and that's authenticity, or being true to yourself. Psychology researchers, like Ken Sheldon and Alex Wood, have been documenting the importance of authenticity for years, mainly by highlighting the perils of inauthenticity. We are all aware of how first impressions play a major role in shaping the way others view us and vice versa; however, it has become a habit to surface act, which means to show what you expect others to see. This usually leads to some work in the background that consumes your energy and leaves you painting an image that you might not be able to sustain for long. This can be seen in the case of new or old employees who keep up the act until stress enthralls them in inner conflict, leading later on to workplace tension.

Surface acting is the exact opposite of resilience; it is in fact a way to live in avoidance of who you are and in fear of what people might think of you. When you are not authentic or genuine, you will immediately start feeling polluted; your reactions will feel strange to others. Your body language will not match your inner thoughts and it will confuse your Being. Conflict starts from within and undulate outwardly to others. You will live in a kind of self-fulfilling prophecy of disagreement and ongoing exhaustion.

Resilience does not mean that we have to go through good and bad events in the same way. It does not mean that we are to fake positivity and happiness. On the contrary, resilience means understanding your own emotions, being mindful of them, and of those around you. I repeat, you do not have to carry other people's psychological luggage, but what you can offer is empathy, compassion and practicing mindfulness to understand what is really going on without absorbing the negativity. I was at some point in my life my own victim. I guarantee it was hellish. I created that hell and I could not understand why I had to deal with any of those tough times. It wasn't until I figured out some of the things that expanded my mode of thought that I saw the light at the end of my tunnel.

It hit me like a bus when I thought that being alive meant that we have to deal with whatever situation we face.

Being alive is knowing that the universe does not discriminate, but only provides us with what focus our intent on. We tend to believe that if we are alive, work hard, push our limits, and make sacrifices that we are entitled to live a perfect life. But have you ever considered that happiness and success are not cosmic rewards that land on your head? The expectation that we will be living a life like in the movies is nothing short of a delusion, which will undoubtedly lead to disappointment and reinforcement of those small bad mental habits.

Being resilient means knowing that we might face situations we would rather not face. Being resilient means knowing that we are not the victims of some sort of cosmic judgment. Resilience also means that your attention is power given to something or someone over you and resilient people are selective in giving their attention. This means that in order to survive, you will have to understand the situation, objectively appraise it so as to know what things you can or cannot change and shift your focus to what you can influence. The more negative attention you give to a situation, such as not being able to perform a task, the more your Being will be blocked from providing you with the energy to fulfill it.

Living in this modern era means that we are constantly faced with threats from a variety of sources. Threats do not count for things that can end a life, but anything that will raise your cortisol levels – that's in physiological terms – meaning that you will have a stressor on your hands. Yet, appraising the situation, knowing that it really is and unveiling its causes will allow you to access the power of tuning into the now and tuning into the frequency of all the good things you have in your life.

I admit that writing this here makes it look quite easy. I know that you are aware of the fact that breaking a bad mental habit is similar to breaking physical habits, which is quite the endeavor. Yet, you need to be reminded that you can do it and that whatever situation you face you must give yourself the permission to access the goodness in you, to be kind with yourself, to choose the words that best work for you.

Put intent into your wish to overcome any situation, be deliberate and give it your best.

Affirmations and imagery are very powerful tools. I will share with you a very simple trick and explain why I have grown fond of this "ritual".

Every night, right before falling asleep, I listen to affirmations with binaural beats. I have the deepest belief and scientific knowledge to back this up. The human brain is known to switch between frequencies, which are: alpha, beta, theta, and delta. Studies have shown that during the first seven years of our lives, children are in a quasi-hypnotic state, hence making them like sponges and allowing any suggestion we give them to be picked up by the subconscious and engraved within the brain. This hypnotic frequency is called Theta and is usually most prominent right before sleeping and upon waking up. This is why I love listening to affirmations during those times since the subconscious is mostly prone to suggestion.

It is well-known that the subconscious mind is more active during sleep, and if there is one way to solve problems and allow positive to become ingrained, it would be through affirmations prior, during and immediately following sleep. You can hack your brain and mind. You can tame them either through conscious effort, or through affirmations. The subconscious mind is incredibly powerful, and once it takes over you when you sleep, you become prone to accepting all kinds of suggestions, which is why I have resorted to using binaural beats and affirmations. In case you cannot sleep while listening to somebody talking, you can do the following:

For the writers and non-writers out there, get a journal or use your smartphone, but I advise you to write with your hand as opposed to typing. Writing by hand has been shown to engage the brain and allow it to develop more neural pathways. So, grab that journal right before you sleep and jot down all your objectives and aims. Make the conscious effort to do some self-talk; ask yourself what you would like to achieve, what you would like to leave behind, what thoughts you want to inspire in people. In short, develop a set of questions, write them down and make it a habit to revisit them. Mentally re-read them and even read them out loud every day. This will surely turn them into your very own custom affirmations.

Try to make sense out of your writings hours after you have written them, your words might carry some insight that you might have never seen before. You will be able to derive new meanings out of your writings, and you will be able to see how your subconscious is at play here. Writing will make it easier for you to scrutinize your strengths and weaknesses. This thought dumping method will make it possible for you to go back and solve problems way more efficiently while making your sleeping time a lot more enjoyable and relaxing. Think of it as unloading your memory into an external hard drive and freely accessing that information at any time.

Our brains affect our bodies; a large body of research was able to show how we can instigate biochemical reactions simply by using our brains. What we imagine can stimulate the body, which will also affect the subconscious. This sheds light on the mind-body connection. I find that it is deeply rooted in situations where the person is traumatized for instance, particularly in Post-Traumatic Stress Disorder (PTSD) cases, whereby patients are usually victims of negative imagery. Their reactions are mostly quite similar, if not identical, to when they were in duress. And so, altering that imagery by understanding the nature of the traumatic experience, understanding its effects on the body and mind, and transforming those mental signals into opportunities for growth will be done through association with better imagery. It is a link shift from negative to neutral or positive.

Our subconscious mind affects our bodies, which in turn will allow us to relive and "re-feel" what we have experienced before. And given that our brains cannot distinguish reality from illusion, we will always react as though we are in that situation. Think of something nice and happy, your prefrontal cortex will rev up, which will allow you to perform more complex cognitive tasks and access deeper cognitive functions. Stressful situations and negative memories/emotions will trigger anxiety periods, and ultimately pull the brakes on some very important processes that take part in your prefrontal cortex. You might have noticed how individuals struggling with depression reach a stage when they do not have the power to leave their rooms, perform simple tasks and even simply enjoy something they used to do before.

Whenever I meet a new patient struggling with depression, I remind myself of the fact that they are not able to see the world the way I do, due in part to the fact that their perception is tainted by negative feelings and associations. The objective with these individuals is to grant them access to their positive emotions and feelings and to alter the biochemical composition of their brains and bodies.

Optimism

What do you think when I mention the word optimism? I bet that you think of a happy-go-lucky person who is constantly cheerful, maybe hyperactive, and possibly smiling all the time like in those utopian musicals. Yet, striving for perpetual cheerfulness is not the way to go. Trying to force yourself into being happy and cheerful has been linked to a constant feeling of disappointment. Life does have its ups and downs, but our outlook and perspective is what shifts the situation from being a problem into being just a situation. Avoiding and suppressing our emotional responses is like forcing your body not to breathe. Emotions are the way our beings inhale and exhale. Dealing with emotions can become quite easy if you think of them as a breath; it enters your body, triggers changes, and then leaves. In other words, emotions come and go as they have a specific timeframe before your mind shifts to other things and to other tasks.

Dissecting your emotions and understanding them has been linked to higher levels of happiness, while avoidance and putting that inaccessible constant cheerfulness state as your objective has been linked to a drop in happiness, even reaching depression.

I have worked with countless patients who have rushed to our rehab centers; they suffered from drug addictions, alcohol addiction, sometimes sexual ones and were unable to understand the dynamics of their ailments. As is the case with any sickness or situations that we go through, the most important piece of the puzzle – that remains missing most of the time in most cases – is awareness. I like to describe a healthy life as a free life, and freedom from the mind does not come at a cost, it comes with added value. The added value of freedom is that you are content and satisfied on a higher level, regardless of the situation you are in because you know that you are well-equipped to face life and see the glass half full. Yet, the human brain; the most complex structure in the universe, is not infallible and is subject to countless ups and downs due to one maladaptive form of coping called avoidance.

Avoidance is poison. I don't mean to talk about that moment when you see the silliness of a situation and decide to overlook it, but those moments when the mind takes over, puts the body on autopilot and tries to outrun from the situation, rather than to deal with it. Avoidance allows mental and physiological toxicity to build in your system. Despite the immediate relief that it may bring, avoidance adds to your stress and – in the case of my patients – exacerbated their symptoms and addictions.

Optimism, in its healthy form, is the conscious act of knowing that life is not constant; it is fathoming that fluctuations are part of life. It is training your eye to perceive the positive in all situations and enjoy the process of dealing with the task at hand. I can mostly say that optimists, true optimists, do not usually judge a situation as being positive or negative, but just enjoy the ride and learn.

Tip: Judge and label things/people less, avoid discriminating adjectives and enjoy the ride.

A Chinese parable perfectly illustrates the above section:

A farmer and his son had a beloved stallion that helped the family earn a living. One day, the horse ran away, and their neighbors exclaimed, "your horse ran away! What terrible luck!" The farmer replied, "maybe so, maybe not. We'll see."

A few days later, the horse returned home, leading a few wild mares back to the farm as well. The neighbors shouted out, "your horse has returned, and it brought several horses home with it. What great luck!"

The farmer replied, "maybe so, maybe not. We'll see."

Later that week, the farmer's son was trying to break one of the mares; however, she threw him to the groundbreaking his leg. The villagers cried, "your son broke his leg, what terrible luck!"

The farmer replied, "maybe so, maybe not. We'll see."

A few weeks later, soldiers from the national army marched through town recruiting all able-bodied boys for the army. They did not take the farmer's son who was still recovering from his injury. Friends shouted, "your boy is spared, what tremendous luck!" To which the farmer replied, "maybe so, maybe not. We'll see."

The story can go on and on, and several other incidents can be added with the farmer replying with the same sentence; however, the morale here is to have a realistic view of life away from pessimism or optimism.

You can either be innately optimist or develop the attitude that carries within it, unwavering hope. Have you ever thought of where the word optimism is derived from? Optimism stems from the Latin root 'optimum' meaning best, it is one of the only and true resilience tools that help individuals live a healthier physical and mental life. Optimism is the ability to adapt to changing situations by seeing how it can serve you best. It is like adjusting your sails as opposed to wishing the wind to change its course.

> *"A man lives by believing something; not by debating and arguing about many things." Thomas Carlyle*

Train yourself to see opportunities in seemingly difficult situations, it's what Winston Churchill preached and practiced. Yet, it must be done in a genuine way, away from the "fake it to make" process. Find the power within to really see, as opposed to simply creating illusions. Once you start becoming a true optimist, you will understand how deeply rooted it is with the concept of abundance, which in turn is linked to acceptance and gratitude for all that you have. Once your mind's eye starts to see the world in terms of situations, rather than problems and a set of happy moments, you will have taken the first step into transforming your reality. Abundance will then pour into your life along with the idea that you have to respect and accept what life has to offer, which will ultimately serve you on the short, medium or long term. Optimism will never be yours if you keep on thinking in terms of what you lack or scarcity. Making it a habit to live life in wonder and gratitude, will spread the magic of abundance in all that you do.

Some might describe the above as being a growth mindset, and it is quite on point because abundance is growth and is the gate to embracing the power that comes with opening your being and allowing it to roam freely. This means holding on to the perspective that goals and aspirations are reachable through effort and practice, rather than determined solely by fate or natural ability. You can find hints all over television series, feature films and books that talk about magic and the power of conjure up things. The majority of those stories, if not all of them, focus on the fact that everything is reachable given that you believe and hold on to positive thoughts. The magic of creating your reality and of being resilient in the face of any situation you face resides within you. The control you exert over your thoughts and your outlook onto the world shape your inner power, your inner resistance to what you *think* are negative events. I must reiterate that I am not talking in terms of denial or avoidance; on the contrary, one must know that there is a situation that one must deal with without judging it as negative or positive. Judgment is a step away from the ability to your brain on problem solving or on enjoying the present moment. My piece of advice is to enjoy the process of problem solving, and not just the solution itself.

I have found a way to be resilient to the clichéd way we humans tend to look at death. It was the time after my father passed away that started to fully understand the connection that joins everything in my environment. My father's absence hit me hard; it was overwhelming and all his struggles, stress, being his mind, chasing work opportunities and businesses suddenly started rushing into my head. So, I started questioning the purpose of life in general and of my own life in particular. I questioned what I really wanted out of my current existence.

The above process led to so many changes and so many decisions. I started thinking about life and death, how to make the best out of my life, and the idea that nothing can be perfectly destroyed has been contested so many times. In short, I believe that nothing can be fully destroyed, and just like electricity we morph from shape to shape, from dimension to another; it's like hopping onto a train and finding yourself at another destination. My father was somehow transported into another dimension whatever and wherever it is. He left his physical body and became everything and nothing at the same time. Try not to pragmatically understand what I am talking about, but instead, feel how loved ones remain everywhere we go. The pain of loss is not to be trifled with or to be joked about, but have you ever considered that what you are feeling is an automatic response to radical change?

Despite my father's passing, I never felt so connected to him as much as I feel right now. The absence of my father in his physical form has pushed me to question many things that I had taken for granted. I felt a sort of obligation to listen to myself, to my body, to my soul and to his immaterial consciousness. I learned not to take everything so seriously; to let go and dissociate myself from my ego and the world around me. So, I detached myself and started letting go of some of my limiting beliefs. This came with accepting the way I am and what I have achieved. With acceptance came the concept of simplicity, which is a complex way of seeing the truth in all its glory. Allow me to explain. Many years ago, I had set objectives and thought that by doing so, I would be doing myself a favor. My thinking revolved around making enough money, proving myself, setting high benchmarks, having properties, investments, companies, being successful and mostly importantly, approval. But death swooped in and altered my vision; I started seeing these things are simple uphill climbs and downhill runs, and so I have seen both sides.

Accomplishments have not given me long-lasting satisfaction. I have discovered that with money comes a whole host of responsibilities and mind-made pressures, and that happiness comes with simplicity. The idea that money does not buy happiness is utterly correct, but there is more to it;

there is a missing part that my father's death has shed light on. Money does not buy happiness, but happiness requires taming money to be of good use and allowing your *Being* to bask in simplicity and wonder.

My father used to tell me that people who give less importance to material possessions seem to look better physically and to function better mentally. I had never thought it true, for I wanted his approval and society's approval. I had never thought, at the time, that the mind uses those material things to create an illusion of hunger and of want. It was after I started becoming my own psychologist, or mentor that I understood how my past, which I cannot change, is affecting me, how my PTSD was pushing me in certain directions and how my hunger for success was fueled by the mere idea that I need to more. This brings me to the idea that the more people have, the more they will want, and the more wants and needs seem lose their distinction. The mind here will be happily jumping all over the place, for it is its mission to keep your being confused and tired.

Time and Death

Time is another fabric, another tool that the mind has created for the sake of enslaving the human race. The good Being within is beyond the concept of time. Yet, the human mind, afraid of its power, has created the fabric of time. The importance of time resides in its practical use, in finishing your tasks and setting you schedule.

Time can be the most powerful tool in our hands because it is, or was, under our own influence and under the power of the Being. Seeing the power of time, the mind has taken over it and created a poisonous chronology leading to death. Time is a sort of consciousness projected outside our bodies. It is the image of the world and how this world functions. Time is your sense of self and your own illusion of the self. If I am to transcribe what time is, I would most certainly consider it as the primordial mind before the mind. It is the element that made us masters of the universe. It *was* the element that made us masters of the universe and we loved it. We came to despise time when we took that bite from the apple and gained knowledge. Once we gained that knowledge, which is not actual knowledge by the illusory distinction between good and evil, we perceived as opposed to saw time as our own. We perceived a made-up injustice of the universe; we started loathing it, seeing it as a way to drain us from our power. We forgot that in the garden of Eden, we were masters of time, masters of purity and masters of the self. We were beyond time, and we were God, with God, within God and God was within us. We were beautiful, really beautiful in the sense that we could not even fit into that adjective. Once we acquired that poison, we showed ourselves out of that garden because we believed we were deserving of a punishment. We became less. Just less and less until the whole world crumbled around us and reality that we had constructed as God became our own torture device. Time was the first thing we hated; we hated the time we grabbed that apple (hypothetically of course), hated ourselves for listening to the serpent, which is the mind, hence us at the same time, hated the taste of knowledge, knowing that we had already possessed it in its pure form, hate the garden because we associated it with that bad incident. We hated time, as simple as that! Once you start hating something, a negative cycle takes over, it starts with the inability to love oneself. Self-loathing is our first sin, and with that came time as we see it. There came time where the second crime against humanity took place as is symbolized by the story of Cain and Abel; the hate of father and mother was replicated and regenerated and ultimately multiplied by physical violence against one of our own kind. Just as Cain killed his brother, he created another instance of time that is based on hatred, jealousy, and shame. This family injustice has no real meaning when compared to the universal law of life. In fact, Cain had protected his brother from what is to come; I do frown upon murder as a whole, but symbolically this story talks of self-murder. Faced with the emerging power of untamed time, the human mind took over us. Cain took nothing but his own life. Reasons are numerous, but I do believe that a man would never take his own life had it been not for a feeling of impotence.

If I am to merge Cain and Abel in one man, I would most certainly be sure that most of us would connect with that new persona. We act as Abel, push ourselves, go to work, *want,* and *need* to give more. We are beings of productivity and purpose. Then comes a time when we feel powerless; our Abel faces Cain, we face a man-made mind and our fight or flight response kicks in. Yet, regardless of what you choose, Cain will always emerge because we became hardwired to either fight and murder the energy that is coming our way or fly away thinking that we are not worth it; we fly away in shame and sometimes with enough jealousy and – a term I particularly dislike – envy, that we wish others ill. Envy is poison to our time and to our *Beings.* It makes us feel inferior to others. We tend to forget that we already possess so much and that our time is rich in experiences driving us towards our objectives.

The fight or flight response might be part of our innate survival kit, but what if we could trigger something else in us. Trigger an immense power that we have and instead of having nothing but negative terms to depict a relatively sad reality, we can observe and know this reality, observe, and know our reaction, dissect everything around us with enough curiosity and love to fathom the intricacies of life. We will then get to know it the proper way and ultimately let our words take center stage. Dealing with reality is dealing with time, and I have had the opportunity to be told various stories of individuals who were fired, abused, left behind, etc., but showed no sadness when let go in the rudest of ways. Time is of the essence, but we must let go of certain aspects of time. I would certainly love to see individuals let go of that which holds them back, let go of what scares them of their future.

We are made to life each passing moment in love, gratitude, happiness, awe, and beauty. As I write this book, my homeland; Lebanon is undergoing deep changes on various levels; the capital Beirut had been destroyed following one of the world's strongest blasts, people were missing/dead, electricity, water, gas, petrol, and other amenities are becoming rare in a country that is constantly on the brink of literal disappearance. Yet, I know that most of my Lebanese fellows have not given up. True thousands have already left the country in search of a better alternative; maybe somewhere they can live in a humane way, but the hope that permeates our Lebanese persona is something that cannot be taken for granted; It is the power to see that time is not something that is out of control. I know that most people do not look at it in that same exact way. The vast majority is not even thinking of it at all, they just want to live, go to work, come back, await the weekend to have some fun and go back to their usual weekdays.

Time frightens most of us. Our minds have been constructed to perceive time in the most toxic way. We are hardwired to allow that mind to look at the calendar, wristwatch, and whatever device you have before your eyes and judge our lives based on the pointing hands of those small machines. We have been morphed into mean machines, not in the positive sense, but in the very limited and stagnating sense, whereby we only feel fulfilled when our mind tells us that we have done enough in a certain period of time. But we are also built to fight the good fight, at least not in throwing fists and destroying each other, but we are built to make a difference. So, I invite you to make the best of time and experience the gentility of time when you let your sense of self experience the present moment.

"Tame your mind, tame time."

I love this expression because it popped into my head while looking out of my window and seeing the rain pour down. Time seemed to be very much like the rain; you could walk through it and allow it to soak you to the bones, blame the whole universe for getting sick and sit in bed pouting for days, or know that it is raining out there, take your umbrella and happily reach your destination.

Time is mind and mind is our creation. We believe that time is running, while it is churning in place. Things seem to be going slow, then hasten to the extent of launching us at the speed of light; however, it is only an illusion. Have you not felt that some days are simply flying by, while others are oozing ever so slowly? It is because once we put our intent into something, just something, we grab time by the hands and dance with it. The way we deal with time has become so subjective because we forget that we can trick time, trick the mind, and influence our reality the way we want it to go.

Time is our creation, the creation of our creation, the creation of our mind to whom we surrendered to. With hating time, we have created our archenemy and have fallen from grace. With that expression in mind, I can say that any book I refer or don't refer to, would surely contain a symbol of a fallen angel, because falling from grace came following a rebellion against our very own divinity. It is quite ironic that we have created our enemy and allowed its spy to manifest itself within us.

"Time and mind are nothing but one."

Ever wondered why and how in Christianity the Holy Trinity was united by love? Ever wondered why it's a trinity? The idea is found in the story that is told of the love between the father and son, which created the Holy Ghost, the fruit of that divine love. The Trinity is the very representation of our divine being seeking to evolve, love itself, accept itself, know itself, see that perfect person in the mirror and allow it to flourish. The Holy Trinity is also reflected in the way we have divided time in hours, minutes, and seconds. Everything around us is usually depicted in threes because our brains retain better everything that is made up of three elements. This simple little trick may pass for something quite silly to our brains that have become ever so used to forgoing all that is obvious. But, let me tell you something, we learn our ABCs, 123s, The Three Musketeers, The Three Stooges, as well as other three-based stories and concepts without batting an eyelash. The number three allows our brains to focus better, once we start going over three, the brain starts to get confused, or it may require more time to process the information, this is why in marketing the optimal number of visual elements is three. If I am to go into design, I can confidently tell you that the basic elements of design are only three (Elements, Fonts, and Colors).

So, it is through the power of three that we can optimally function, retain and talk. Most of us tend to use three examples when writing because it feels *good*, and it rightly does. We are built on what I would like to call the Rule of the Universal Threes. Sigmund Freud's attempts at understanding the mind, has shed light on something that I would love to share, and that is the power of two. According to Freud, the mind prefers the number two because threes can bring around jealousy. Imagine two life partners receiving their first baby, a team of two welcoming a third member, etc. the mind's overthinking usually starts to kick in, and this is where psychoanalysis failed to perceive the importance of going beyond the mind and considering the being as the original source of information, rather than the ailment-ridden mind. Freud has surely made great breakthroughs in understanding the mind, but it was all based on illnesses, what causes this issue, what resolves this other issue, but none of his work was focused on the science of happiness. Despite my love for psychology in all its subdisciplines, I believe that our brains and beings are way too connected to a divine entity that is within and without to fully understand what is going on. This brings me to the issue of death. There is nothing scarier than the thought of losing one's own life. The energy that courses through us, the resolve that moves our limbs, the strength to lift things, lift the morale of others and change the course of history itself is what makes our life force. We value things on this earthly plane, and we give everything a certain timeframe. With that specific timeframe comes a certain end to things, and an end of human beings in the form of passing to another dimension.

As a child growing up in a war-torn country, I have seen people lose their lives in the fraction of second. I was mentally unprepared to see human bodies torn to shreds. It was a terrifying view, and I can't but cringe at the idea that humans can do such things to each other. Yet, despite the terror and the PTSD (Post Traumatic Stress Disorder) – that still causes me to jump whenever I hear a loud sound or anything that resembles gunshots – I have come to accept the ultimate transformation of the body; that of death.

People try to outrun the timeframe that we call death as though life is a race. But let me tell you the truth that is and that will never change; time and death are one, the more you look for time, the more you look for death. Instead of looking for extra moments, instead of stressing about finalizing that task and instead of blaming your failure on the lack of time, find a purpose for what you are doing. We all say that we are living in the fastest era. True! Things are becoming much faster; however, time is not running, time is flowing, and we nudge it; we can even control it. Being gods and having God within is the image I want you to help engrave in your head. God created everything in seven days; why would you want to change the universe in less than seven seconds? If God, the Word took His time to create light; you, that beautiful energy at the end of his creation endeavor, wouldn't it be wise of you to listen to God within and create what is of value after setting everything in place at the right pace?

In today's world human values have become somewhat blurred. Everything has become so easily reached; food, entertainment, distant countries, etc. But where are we heading to? Have you ever thought that with that ease of access, you are losing some core values that are crucial to your mental health? We are packing our internal God into a small box, labeling it, and locking it inside a few pages, words and thoughts and seem distant. We forget that God is compassion, acceptance, respect, sincerity, and unconditional love. God *is* you and is a set of values that live on and are timeless; this is why God is immortal. Your mental health is not something to joke about. This statement might sound a bit too serious, maybe a bit scary because according to the human mind's view of the expression *mental health*, humans are subject to mental ailments and are on this earth to suffer. How many times have

I heard that same degrading statement? I have never found any retort until I was inspired to write this book. If you are here to suffer, then how is it possible for so many to tap into the God within and manifest a beautiful life?

The magic is there in the few words that I have mentioned above; compassion, acceptance, respect, sincerity and unconditional love. These are the five basic elements of a beautiful life. A beautiful life is the product of living by immortal values and by the application of self-appreciation. I might have used the word God numerous times so far, but these three little letters stand for *Grand (or Good) Orthopractic Design*.

This was even covered by the late Stephen Hawking who used his massive knowledge to realize knowledge as inherited by the Greeks, Nicolaus Copernicus, and so on. He has considered the move from the mythological to the scientific, the issue of free will of scientific determinism, the observer-dependent reality, elegance in science, the subatomic scale and its conception of the world, the revolutionized view of time and space, the expansion of the universe, and so on. I will not attempt to summarize that beautiful work, but it can summarize how everything we do can be seen as our very own design, our own grand design where reality is the product of our own efforts. I will provide a simple explanation rather than an intricately scientific one.

Every single one of those five values must start with you applying them to yourself. To expand your being and fathom the divine entity within, you ought to be compassionate towards yourself. Words fail to depict the actual action but describe the feeling of warmth towards oneself. Once you truly become compassionate towards your being, this warmth will be reflected upon others and your divine light (again back to the light) will shine outwardly. It is quite on point to go back to the Book of Genesis and understand the primordial meaning of the darkness and void prior to the act of creation. God was alone, I was alone, you were alone, and by being alone you become introspective. The act of introspection is one that will lead you to view your *self* and your feelings in the confines of the primordial void. The water is your mirror and it reflects your truth, your true image. As part of your effort to understand your feelings and emotions, we look at our reflection and attempt to make sense of our constitution, and just like God, we ought to overflow with self-compassion, self-acceptance, self-respect, sincerity, and unconditional self-love. As your being is filled with such joyful and powerful elements, everything around receives unlimited energy and value.

Once we become God and God becomes us, death is no longer a frightful sight and just like the demons we face, we befriend it. Death is no longer the end of us, it is not a beginning either, it is the gate through which we *pass* onto the real dimension of truth. As I write this book, millions of my cells are dying, I know that this sounds frightening, but it's only the truth. Death has had quite the sad history to say the least. It had been represented by some dark entity, the reaper, hades, some kind of angel; it has been personified over and over again in an attempt to belittle it or just make it even more frightening. Either way, just like God, we went from looking at it as an integral part of our being, to ascribing a few letters to this rather simple, yet complicated process that we undergo.

Death is an ongoing process; it had started when we symbolically defied God within and picked the red shining apple. Let's not blame anything else but ourselves for that little act, since the snake that we ever so hate for being the cause of our fall, is none other but our own mind. The tricks that our mind plays on us plague our being with an avalanche of images and emotions that are just illusions. Our human mind tends to look at life in a contradictory way; in fact, it considers life through its own limited field of vision. I know for a fact that you feel at least slightly uncomfortable thinking about this topic. This is understandable given the overly grim image that we have painted of death. Come to think of it, we have transformed it into a dark and unfathomable thing. But, have you ever thought about death as truth that just is? Have you ever regarded it in an objective way? I mean to say that if you bypass your mind's tricks and limiting beliefs regarding yourself and the world around you, death will be another stage and a summons by the universe.

Acceptance of death does not come by easily just by telling yourself that death is okay. The idea of you thinking that way actually spreads joy in your soul; however, there are stages that you ought to go through to reach the results and state of mind that you seek, not to mention morph it into a sustainable mode of thought.

We allow limiting beliefs to control our daily lives; from our first conscious thought in the morning to the ones that run amok at night, we grant them access to our most precious treasures; our freedom. I may have mentioned it, but it is vital at this stage to mention that we are born shackle-free. This means that our newly formed brains are not grasped by the symbology that surrounds us. As babies we do not know the difference between life and death; we know one thing, and that is that we are. We live the truth for a brief moment, and everything seems to be going quite well. During our development, our brains start to be shaped by our parents, friends, community, society, and all that we ingest in vision and sound. With this large amount of data being poured into our Being, everybody else's man-made mind infects our pure being, causing it to grow a tumor, and that tumor becomes larger as time goes by. As this ailment reaches its maturity, it would have taken the copied shape of the being; a crooked copy of what is. Our brains start listening to that strange entity. It gives it attention, hence power, and no longer pays heed to real attention. Our Being and our brains drown neck-deep in what we lovingly call a *comfort zone*. Despite the fact that this zone looks comfortable, we *know* how bad it is to restrain our being from taking the risks it needs. These are not risks that bring about danger, but rather essential actions that allow what just is to flourish. Yes! We *know* that we are just choosing the smallest room to sit in, while the universe waits.

So, with limiting beliefs, we become infused with commonly agreed to ideas. It is like catching the flu or a cold. Everybody can catch a cold or a flu, but some individuals are just plain stronger than others and fight it, while some go through the aches and pains of being sick. Even though there are so many variables that differentiate both situations, fighting limiting beliefs; what images others paint of you, is no walk in the park. It is rather a walk in the woods of your subconscious mind and becoming more and more aware of the ideas that are growing like fungus on those beautiful trees. You will, at some point, reach dark, scary areas, and you will have to have to stroll across them like a good soldier to face your demons. There will be so many mirages and illusions, and you need to fight those illusions. Forget that you are called Robert, Jane, Mohammed, Eli. Forget the image that others have painted of you. Look at yourself in the mirror, and instead of using adjectives to describe yourself, bask in the glory of your being that *just is*. You are what you are, and nothing can change that. There is no adjective to describe the creator that resides within. Focus on pretermit feelings that arise from human depictions of processes that just are. Abandon your fears and then regard death from the point of view of someone who has passed on. Let go of preconceptions of heaven and hell, for they are human depictions of what you create for yourself, and rather focus all our intent, life force and beautiful divine attention on the natural state of death, of passing on.

If you are able to let go of all that clutter and noise for a few minutes, you will have achieved a breakthrough. This means you have taken a step beyond the infantry of the mind or human defense mechanisms. You have stepped on that slithering denial, you have taken anger by the horns, and you have won that bargaining battle and found acceptance of the inevitable.

I had never thought of visualizing this world without me; I had never attempted to visualize how my absence would impact others, how they would talk of me and how my life's work would be viewed. Once I started visualizing this material world without me, I understood that I was nothing but a speck of dust in this universe; a powerful one, but still small enough to be nothing. I had mentioned that humans can be nothing and everything; humans can be the most powerful magnets if they allowed their Beings to shine, and black holes of greed and want if they allowed their minds to take over.

With my father's passing, I learned to let go of the concept of connecting to everything in life and once I accepted the fact that I am going to die and leave everything I did behind, that I am only going to be remembered by how my Being touched others, how I connected to others with love and understanding, with compassion and empathy that I was able to become more immune to my mind's attacks. You can have a connection with all things around you, but not to the extent of making them the center of your existence. In fact, I have learned that nothing, but your Being should be the center of your existence; the sun does not rely on the planets around it to shine, it relies on its core; that beautiful burning core that radiates outwardly and gives unconditionally. The cycle of life and death is something grand to consider, it allows us to let go of all things that are unnecessary and to acquire only that will be of added value to our core. I still remember quite vividly how I was feeling when I was gathering my late father's things and packing them to be sent away; I felt so small in this expanding universe, and things felt so trivial compared to what we leave as a legacy.

While going through his old things and giving them away, the only thing he left was what the people thought about him and the moments he spent with them.

Dying before dying means letting go and accepting that one day we will be gone. Humility plays a major role in this feeling, and as I had mentioned before, feeling like a small speck in this universe entails accepting the fact that we are going to leave this body and transcend our existence and consciousness to another level, to another realm. It is then healthier to live a simpler life; one that is filled with genuine joy, wonder, and most importantly love. Such a life is linked to the realization that everything will degrade over time, that humans will pass on and that we ought to think of the purpose of the soul in this life.

What is my soulful and mindful purpose in this life?
How can I make all things around me tools to support that purpose?

Yet, simplicity is complex and the realization that nothing of the material world will serve us later in the other dimension can scare many of us. A helpful thought here would be to ask ourselves about the purpose of our soul in this life, what is our energy's purpose. When we think in terms of our energy's purpose, we start understanding why we felt drained while doing something that, according to our societal limiting beliefs, is good for us, brings us stability – as many of us would think about employment – and instant gratification. But is instant gratification or the satisfaction of a very punctual need our life's and energy's purpose. I have already mentioned that the purpose of us being here is to be useful. But to be useful, you have to understand where your energy lies, where it is drained, what makes you tick and what destroys you. Accept simplicity and focus on the relationships with people and to give something, which is more valuable; giving love and satisfaction and contentment, having fun, enjoying the journey and not just chasing wrong things.

This is what I see in patients who come for a variety of reasons, which I call symptoms, such as depression, addiction, anxiety, trauma and so on. Many do not have real purpose; many do not have meaningful connections in life; they feel lonely or lose track of their lives. Such individuals will have to find themselves first and understand the concept of self-love and self-acceptance before moving up the scale of a healthy life. I was talking to a friend of mine the other day. This person had made it as a successful businessman. Yet, as we sat and chatted, I felt that he was itching to tell me something, and when probed him, he let out a sigh and simply said that he felt purposeless. I probed him even further until he spilled the beans. Despite all the success that he had enjoyed, and probably still enjoys, this man has lost his sense of purpose following the sale of his business. He was not resilient. In fact, he had not built a robust foundation for his personal life because he was married to his work.

When I think about resilience, this thought comes to mind: the simpler I try to build my life, the more I practice acceptance and self-love. This creates in me a calmer personality since I am no longer looking for approvals, for changing the way others perceive me and for materialist gains or anything that is in the outer world. This keeps me in balance inwardly, outwardly and on the soul level. This has built my resilience in such a way as to make everything that seems to be difficult to deal with a passing situation.

At a certain time in my life, I was a perfectionist. I had mentioned how I was chasing all those approvals, applause, and materialistic things. I was difficult to handle and to deal with, which tended to be problematic for those around me. Perfectionism does not necessarily mean a good thing. Put yourself in my shoes for an instant; imagine that you want something to be done, imagine for just one moment that you have a vision in your brain/mind that you want to achieve. Be a perfectionist, try to imagine how difficult it is for perfectionists to accept anything but that they have pictured. Being a perfectionist means staying victim of your mind and of the way it is belittling your being by saying that nothing is perfect in this earthly realm.

The issue with perfectionism is that it is chasing the unreachable, and I was trapped in that cycle for a long time. Was I happy? Not really! I was in fact always thinking of ways to make things work the way I wanted them to work. I was even impatient with my loved ones and when things did not go as expected, I would feel disappointed, even angry. My employees did their best, but I was never satisfied until my father's death opened my eyes.

With that blow to my mind, I felt like a newborn; the light from actual reality was blinding. I looked around after his passing and saw that everything had been altered. My perception of the world around me was not the same anymore. I had spent years battling illusions and shallow happiness, whereas joy had always been right under my nose. I had a beautiful family, a beautiful home, flourishing businesses, and a great future ahead. My eyes were just blinded by my mind's inner workings, by feelings of lack despite the abundance I was living in.

I packed my father's belongings, sent them away and pushed myself to stand before a mirror and spoke to myself. At first, my mind was telling me that what I was doing was madness; it laughed at me, and I couldn't look at myself in the eye. That was my challenge; to look myself in the eye and forgive myself first for not being there for myself, for my family and for my entourage that needed me.

With this, I tapped into my resilience, my soul's resilience to society's limiting beliefs. So, instead of looking at my life as a series of challenges, I saw them as opportunities; instead of using words for the sake of using them, I started making sense of every word I said to those around me and instead of chasing material possessions, I was not grateful for all that I had. I had built a life I was thankful for, and my soul found peace when my eyes perceived the importance of leaving a legacy for those that matter most first, and for the world second.

Acceptance

Life is beautifully unpredictable; it is something that we usually take for granted as the energy of that word seems to be a little lower than that of, for instance, resistance, power, and so on. We are deeply energy-bound Beings, and to make things a little more interesting the universe threw in that massive part of our constitution that is called the subconscious. Why am I mentioning the subconscious at this stage? It is because we are our environment and we are all that we get from what we focus our attention on, what we consciously listen to, what we hear, what we see in our hindsight and what touches us, or others, physically. I am the product of an environment that was war-torn; I had left my homeland at the age of seven in the hopes of leaving behind all those booming explosions, the fear, and every negative heavy accessory the war and my society had put on my back.

Upon my arrival to Switzerland, the little Middle Eastern child that stepped into the classroom was not welcome. I had expected, or at least daydreamed that things will immediately be better. It was definitely much better in terms of the peace that you perceive upon stepping there, but it was a different vista from a child's perspective; I thought I would be welcomed with arms wide open by a bunch of cute little kids, be allowed to tell my stories and grow a circle of friends that would act as my safety net.

How would a child think this way? Isn't it a reflection
of what you are feeling now? How is this related to acceptance?

A child is not oblivious, especially a child who was swept away from war into sudden peace. A child does not think in terms of psychology and in terms of life events, a child sees a story and would love to tell it, listen to it, live it and dream about it. That's all that I did. I sit sometimes thinking of that moment when I saw my grandparents bidding us goodbye, them crying, neighbors looking at us with a little, or much envy, because they rightfully felt the need to leave this constant warzone, the way the house looked dim and dark as we all gathered our bags and headed off towards the car, I could hear the distant rumbling of explosions, the fear gripping me at the throat, the heaviness that comes with the destruction of things.

I resisted these emotions, I thought it better to live in avoidance - not that I understood the concept of avoidance in any way – but it felt good to avoid that sadness and fear, maybe tune out what warring factions were doing to each other and run away. When I looked back at my grandparents waving at us as the car taking us to the airport drove away, my little being felt torn yet at ease as well, but that was just short-lived. Explosions felt a little closer, snipers sat watching, perched on top of buildings, my mother's breath was shallow, and my dad was extremely tense. A blast shook me, mom shrieked, dad ground his teeth and kept his calm. At this point of my story, I was sucking in all the energy around me, from fear to wanting to leave the country and escape this never-ending game of deathly ping-pong.

I resisted my feelings, I made it clear to others that I was strong enough to be my own little man and at school, I put up with a lot of bullying, booming words describing me in ways I never thought of. The dark-haired little boy was the dark sheep of the class. I resisted even more; my emotions were building up inside me. I didn't want them there; I wanted to be free, but something else had its claws in me, but I did not know how to label it, until another student in my class caused a loud noise. I violently jumped, my heartrate spiked, I started to sweat and memories of moments of deep, poisonous fear emerged within me. I do not recall what happened next, but I do know that I relived scenes of war in my head, and my brain took them as real incidents.

When I think back on these little things that were shaping me at the time, I still feel that they are relevant, as they should. The past is definitely not changeable, and I would not trade anything or any moment or any person just to alter my childhood. What I was describing now, surely contains elements of my past, younger self, as well as elements of my present, more mature being who bear a hidden wound, or, in other terms, carries the little silently screaming child. In between the two, the teenager that I grew up into, carried the rebellious, extremely driven person who wanted to prove himself to others, who disliked his background, disliked his current situation, and disliked the fact that he had to go through war and escape bombs, while boys and girls from other countries were happily playing. For a long period of time, I did not want to talk about it; I felt the wound, heard the scream, denied the fact that it was my inner voice and my psychological body asking for help, but I had what I'd like to call the 'Katniss' syndrome, I felt like I had to keep everything inside and face my own version of the Hunger Games.

In my current state, I transformed my PTSD into something useful, rather than a heavy chain around my neck. Objectively thinking about PTSD, means looking at it as a rearranging of the brain, or the neural networks as a response to a major stressor. This means that you can survive in dangerous situations while the brain, which does not differentiate between negative and positive experiences, will be adapting and reordering its neurons and intelligently becoming more efficient. So, with that in mind, I need you to trust your brain, trust your being, trust your whole constitution because you were designed to survive and thrive.

I turned my PTSD into something that I can use. What happened to me reminded me of a discovery in the 1980s when Richard Tedeschi and Lawrence Calhoun, at the University of North Carolina, found that trauma changed the majority of their subjects' lives for the better. I turned Post-Traumatic Stress Disorder into Post-Traumatic Growth; it sounds better, it feels better, and it *is* actually better than keeping yourself in a loop of negative thoughts and reactions. Your brain has rearranged itself and has evolved; this is change, and we tend to resist change. From a psychological standpoint, growth begins with healing yourself and understanding that we must go through certain situations, that our brains do not know the difference and that we are describing these situations through our mind's lens, and we all know how sadistic and masochistic can be. The way to go from here is to go with the situation, accept it, build your strength based on the momentum of the events surrounding you. Once you let go and drift into the deep end of your Being's power, the strength you acquire will be tremendous.

Once I accepted that what I had gone through will never change, that became my strength and without it I wouldn't be me – without judging that potential self as better or worse – I accessed self-love and self-acceptance, I conquered my fears and I understood that trauma and the way that we talk about it has been considered from a single point of view. The process of acknowledging that you have been through trauma and befriending that event or those situations is tedious, understanding your inner mechanisms is even more challenging, exhausting at times, but utterly beautiful. You will have to battle stress hormones released into your bloodstream, control your reactions, think of ways to shed light on what seems dark within and create a safe passageway for your emotions to be expressed. With the prefrontal cortex, the amygdala and hippocampus witnessing or having witnessed change, the adrenal gland, the hypothalamus and the pituitary gland start pouring those stress hormones to instigate a flight, fight or freeze response. Why? Because we tend to resist what our environment is giving us by dubbing them as positive and negative, happy and sad, good and bad. We judge so much; it poisons our souls.

Once you stop resisting and accepting the variety of situations that you have faced and will face without listening and watching the scenarios created by the mind, you will understand how peace and adaptation are intertwined. We might even call it surrender, but not in the way you might think of it. The image I have in my head is not of a sad surrender to facts and situations of life, it's not remaining passive, on the contrary, it is opening your eyes to what you might learn, understanding how and why you are reacting and floating along with the current, trusting the process, trusting your body and brain as they are wonderfully equipped to handle everything. You might feel that the stress we feel at a certain time makes us look tired, or feel physically and emotionally exhausting, these are just signs that you are evolving and adapting; it takes energy, it takes tremendous amounts of energy to become who you are.

If a situation is causing you a lot of stress, thinking intelligently is your way out, you will have to learn to see the clues, understand the signs that your body is sending you and understand the tricky language of your mind in order to master yourself. I have learned that my trauma is my strength, that once I understood how it affected me, instead of thoughtlessly jumping at loud noises, I can now think more rationally despite the response and recognize the cause of that sound for instance. I no longer resist all that is externally trying to help me adapt, and I no longer judge by categorizing those situations and stimuli.

Reaching self-mastery is an arduous path, you can find yourself looking pristine on certain days thanks to a number of breakthroughs and discoveries, or because you had an uneventful day, and sometimes, you'd find yourself all torn and adapting, in pain most probably and wanting to rest, but this is just your being expanding and your consciousness and emotional intelligence reaching new heights.

In the conventional way of thinking, acceptance is as a negative response to stress. Yet, as studies have shed more light onto the processes that govern the human psyche, acceptance has been seen as the focus of therapies; the recognition and acceptance of one's conscious and unconscious issues are crucial for reaching self-mastery.

Speaking of acceptance, my brain felt flooded with all the things that I did not like about myself, until I learned to respect and love the being that I am. Once acceptance washes over us, our acceptance of the other, which also comes under the term respect, makes it easier for us to relax and radiate with unconditional love, for what is unconditional love if we cannot accept ourselves unconditionally? And what is unconditional love without the full acceptance of the other?

I cannot stress the importance of acceptance as the final and most important step towards proper self-recognition. Acceptance is an eye-opener; it removes the lens that society has forced upon our eyes. I am not here to judge whether this lens is providing you with a better image of yourself, or a worse one, I am attempting to inculcate a healthier way of seeing yourself, seeing your true self in the mirror and accepting everything that you are. Accept what you thought was ugly and beautiful, remove the labels and shift your focus from the physical to provide some space for your soul and being to relax and fill what the material world was trying to fill.

Buddhism, for instance, has always seen acceptance as the ultimate key to happiness, and in more modern times, the 12-step treatment for alcoholism, as established in 1939, set acceptance as a foundation for a happier and sober life. As I have said earlier, acceptance is very far from being passive surrender, but an effort that requires a lot of fortitude that has roots in motivation to reach a better self. This equation falls under mindfulness, as accepting yourself and deploying efforts to better yourself, requires a whole lot of awareness and being mindful of how your egoic mind is trying to destroy all that you want to become. As I have mentioned before, you have to tame time, to tame your mind and with practicing such positive actions, you will become a calmer and emotionally balanced person who lives in a constant state of presence.

Acceptance is your only weapon against how your mind paints the world around you; your mind will always try to fit you into a little square, not even a box; a tiny square to limit you from all sides, but most importantly to hinder your three-dimensional growth. Your mind does not want you to become God and to tap into your being, and so with acceptance of what is and who you are without labeling yourself, without using adjectives to judge yourself, you will be able to reach calmness and inner balance. The dissociation from your mind and the dissociation from what you have learned on the physical realm will lead you into moments of enlightenment that will increase in frequency and intensity.

With acceptance relieving the pressure inside, you will be able to see the world as it is. You will no longer need to say that this thing is good, and that other thing is bad. Your Being will just perceive its environment and enjoy all that is around it away from the constant noise that the mind generates. Imagine the following: you are living in a very noisy neighborhood – if you are, then you will be able to relate. If not, then try to imagine – yet you have a nice view. As the noise pollutes your ears, your eyes always rest on the greenery outside. You sigh and think of the trees, the flowers, the calmness that is supposed to be out there, and wish the noise would lessen.

In this case, you see the nature, you know it is there, but you cannot feel it; you cannot connect to something that is or seems aloof. Your mind then just squeezes what you see outside your window into a little corner and your view of what is outside becomes one of association with the physical form. You will not feel calm, and your mind, which is constantly buzzing will make things worse for you. You will feel like you want to fight the noise, nag about it, or simply forget that you can take action and find a solution.

Acceptance is when you close the window and tune out the noise; it is that moment when you are able to reach emotional balance, understand that the struggles that you have been through have just made you more emotionally intelligent and that you are a work in progress.

There is no destination, only objectives.

Once you master acceptance and keep judgment away from your Being, you will be able to handle situations in ways you never thought you would. Here's one of those stories that keep me in check; my family and I had planned this beautiful vacation to an island near Abu Dhabi. Everything and everyone were ready for the trip of a lifetime, and let me tell you, that trip had taken some real planning since we wanted to have the perfect vacation. Friends of ours planned also to go to a nearby hotel, so they packed their bags, bought their tickets, and made their bookings. On the day of the trip, things seemed to spiral out of control with our friends; they were not able to travel because of passport issues. Of course, they were furious, they did not know what to do and instead of finding a solution, they just headed home fuming, probably blaming the whole universe for that little mishap. It wasn't long before my daughter faced the same situation. She was not allowed to board the flight for the same reason as my friends', so my wife and I considered our options, and trust me, it was not easy to control our reactions, but seeing our family and weighing the options, I did. I asked myself: what can I do to properly handle this situation. I figured I had two options:

- ♦ Go back home, postpone the trip and plan things better next time
- ♦ Find a flight to another destination that would accept my daughter's passport close expiry date

My wife and I opted for the second option; that vacation was not going to elude us as we were focused on achieving our objectives and go on a fun vacation. So, we agreed to reorganize our trip and go to the Maldives the same day and finally found ourselves spending an exceptional time there.

There are some scientific facts that I have come establish as personal life rules, the most prominent of which was to live a life away from simply and purely being emotional. We are human beings at the end of the day but living solely on emotions and acting based who those chemical reactions that bottle up in our bodies will not help anybody reach a solution. In fact, emotional reactions, hence overreactions, are the base of much conflict around the world, save the ones that are strategically planned. I shall not talk about these but be sure that strategically planned conflict is also was instigates emotional reactions in human beings. Think in terms of the various dictators who have plagued whole populations throughout history.

Again, living a life away from emotions starts with not judging the situation as good or bad; it is felt rather than understood, and implemented through the wisdom of allowing your Being to objectively cut through the mind's noise, accept what is and make way for solutions to emerge out of the darkness.

Acceptance paves the way for a better and more funny life, while self-love and acceptance alter the past into a learning experience.

FINAL THOUGHTS

Reading this book is a three-phase process and might require going back to certain sections over and over again and making use of repeated information, which serve as reminders. If you have reached this part and are about to finish this book, congratulations, you have just graduated out of the first stage of understanding self-mastery, and starting your journey, which might lead to numerous decisions, inspiration, further studies, digging deeper and researching the various tools that will allow you to tap into the divine self that is concealed within and I thank you for your diligent attention.

Look at this book as your little rehab, just know however, that reading the words and trying to understand them purely with the mind is not sufficient. You must start implementing your new routines step by step to the point where your thoughts, spoken words, and the feelings you receive are inline.

How? By balancing the topics in this book, your physical, mental, social, and spiritual health. Start with:

- ◆ Analyzing and understanding yourself
- ◆ Define your vision & personal purpose
- ◆ Defining your long-term and short-term actions
- ◆ Set up a balanced weekly routine schedule

As you might have noticed, this book is the product of my personal and professional experience; it is the fruit of many years of struggle, experiencing ups and downs, learning about me, understanding, and learning about others and making that knowledge work for my benefit and for those I care most about.

Upon reading this last section, I would like you to think about three main criteria, which are our thoughts, how we think about ourselves, about others, if anxiety is plaguing our Beings, how ideas and thought processes are altered and impact our daily lives, followed by what we talk about, which is intimately linked to our thoughts as our interactions are produced by thoughts and images that we perceive within our brains. Interactions with others are clear signs of whether we have been providing our being with the balance it needs in terms of physical, social, mental, and spiritual health.

I keep on mentioning that having a routine is of utter importance because it is one of the most grounding and relaxing tools. You can create eating routines, develop good exercise patterns, set up appropriate sleep schedule and so on, which will all play a vital role in allowing your body and brain to recover, hence bolstering your spiritual health. The equation is simple and just as you need to take rest after a rigorous workout, your brain and consequently the soul or being will have to take a breath and recover from the emotional workouts that you undergo.

Case in point, my wife and I decided to drastically change our lives and even root ourselves in a new place. Here, I would like to focus on the importance of having a partner that is on the same wavelength as you are. This is easier said than done; we have all met so many people that we thought might make good partners but let me share with you one obvious piece of advice; there is no such thing as a perfect partner. It is not a mathematical equation that we can solve; a perfect partner comes with acceptance and respect. Acceptance and respect might be viewed as one entity, which also requires maturity as the X factor to activate the previously mentioned two compounds. This brings acceptance and living happily into the realm of chemistry; a term that is so widely used and abused. Yes! Chemistry is the process by which we can establish whether two people are compatible, but this should preferably be done away from pure subjectivity, or the mind's influence.

Going back to our mutual decision to move away from Switzerland, I can confidently say that this was one of the most complex decisions to consider, for it involved us taking into account us as a couple, our children's ability to cope and adapt, ways to make the transition easy, ways in which this move might impact our decision, among other things. To keep the story short, we wanted to our children to enjoy an environment that is accessible to them, and by environment, I mean nature; everything that is alive and thriving on its own. The autonomy of nature in its beautiful cycle is inspiring, so we sought to provide our children with the opportunity to experience what it feels like to be in nature.

We moved into a farmhouse in Mallorca, Spain. It was not long before our ears whistle less, our heads buzz less with thoughts, our eyes and facial muscles relax with every breath and something deep within take up a space we never thought we had. That space was in fact the inability to relax while pushing away fatigue, anxiety, and the impact of urban life on our Beings. We set up an environment for ourselves that serves our higher purpose, and thanks to the presence of various animals within the farm, we are able to live linked to nature everyday.

With that relaxing environment being established, we found a school that fit our vision, which leads me into talking about how important it is to understand the curricula provided by the various institutions, tap into the strengths of our children, allow them to express their innermost thoughts and stay active on various fronts that I have already mentioned.

This bouquet of decisions came with a higher level of change in my professional life; I have long been working in the finance field, which had me living a great life. Yet, as you might expect, this was not enough, as I was not looking for financial gains only, I was not satisfied with the immediate gratification that such profit brought about, and I felt a pressing need to change this part of my life. So, I honed in on my passions, found ways to help others and ultimately give back to the universe after receiving so many blessings.

This professional change came with me pioneering a treatment program in Mallorca. The treatment is a big success, and the team that I set in charge of this treatment knows what I wanted this program to include. This was a very intimate process, since developing a treatment program is not only about going through the science of the mind, the science of brain and the science of the body, developing a treatment program goes through the creator's very self and is based on his understanding of the struggles that come around with anxiety, addiction in all its forms, depression, and all the other ailments that may befall us.

Establishing a treatment is a learning experience with a steep learning curve, which can either show that your set plan will have a positive effect or not. I have based that treatment on everything I have been through, from my struggle to establish myself as a businessman, further studies, to my readings, my experience with various treatment centers, meeting professionals, seminars, research, and my belief that the individuals I have selected to care for others will make a team that will function like a well-oiled machine.

Since then, I have felt an overwhelming sense of satisfaction. I guess, this was part of the legacy that I wanted to leave behind; one that speaks of a soul that cared for others, but most importantly, knew what that other soul is going through and fathomed the intricacies of what life what throw at you. My passion for human life is what keeps me going; it is what keeps me going, alongside my family, my partnership with my wife, as well as my business life.

Throughout this book, I have talked about the importance of a healthy body, not just for the esthetics, but also for its impact on the psyche, the soul and social performance, which leads me to mention in this final section that our move to Mallorca came with a firm belief that a shift in scenery, exposure to more sunlight, life in nature and a quieter ambiance and more space were much needed. This has morphed into an opportunity to do things as a family, starting with purchasing the right ingredients and being conscious of the source, hiking together, horse-riding across the beautiful landscape in Mallorca, growing our own vegetables and fruits, establishing a connection with nature, and expanding our mindfulness link with the energy around us. Following this change in lifestyle, my children have come to understand that everything is connected in a simple way and shored up through simple acts of kindness, love, good intent, and mindfulness.

I was surprised at how much we have all understood the importance of acceptance as the final ingredient to a happier life. It goes without saying that there will always be annoying situations; moments where you think that life is unfair, meet irritating people, face dead ends and so on. But is it the situation and the people that are instigating such feelings, or is it our own internal chemistry and our interaction with the external world? It is crucial to understand what is pushing our bodies and minds to act and react in certain ways since we are not soulless machines, but conscious beings that strive to reach a higher level.

Whenever you are faced with any situation that might seem dire or simply irritating, take three deep breaths, expand your diaphragm, which is the dome shaped muscle that allows you to inhale and exhale by contracting and releasing, and tell ask yourself whether what you are going to do next is the right and fair thing. Whenever I reach the point where I feel I will react badly, I take a second to visualize myself after I have properly resolved the situation, I push my mindfulness muscle a little further and try to understand my body's and mind's reaction to what I have at hand. I become the master of myself, not in the sense that I act like a warden and jail my emotions. No! This would be avoidance and denial; instead, I become the scientist and artist behind the work of art that will be my next action. Thinking that way feels like you have so much space within your being, not an empty space, but one that is filled with the one thing that we all wish for, peace, contentment, and satisfaction. You should know that satisfaction that comes after a mindful observation of yourself is way more fulfilling than the immediate gratification of a thoughtless reaction.

You have the power to apply this in all aspects of your life. I have already mentioned that at some point in my life, I have become quite irritable, aggressive, and thought of life as a convoluted web of inexplicable alterations. Yet, after years of adventuring through muddled feelings, unfathomable emotions, and physical hindrances, I have understood the importance of keeping steady energy levels across all situations.

Be yourself no matter the situation; altering your behavior and only showing your best is not human. But what is your best? Come to think of it, if we are created, or have evolved into what we are now means that we are to accept our constitution, accept our ups and downs. This also means that we can accept the fact that we are able to embrace the power of radical acceptance, which will lead us into accepting life as it is rather than just looking at life as a source of suffering. Once you practice radical acceptance, you look at life in a factual fashion, understand and change what you can control while dealing with what you cannot. In order to reach radical acceptance, you can start by observing your mind and being mindful of when it starts questioning reality. This could be through simple thoughts, such as:

Why me?
Why is it this way?
Why am I the recipient of bad luck?

Watching your mind for such thoughts is the first step to knowing that you are fighting an invincible opponent, yourself, because you are the creator of your own reality and fighting this reality is going into a fight against yourself. It is a thoughtless reaction that you can do without.

Think and use your brain's power. Once observation becomes ingrained as one of your healthy habits, you will need to remind your brain that some situations cannot be altered and that things happen following a certain external stimulus or action. Then look at yourself in the mirror, or visualize yourself, see the true image of your Being within, your true physical form because we tend to forget that we are beautiful Beings and that what is inside is reflected outwardly, practice self-talk, breathe and use positive imagery.

Lastly, I advise you to think of times you reacted in ways you did not find adequate, how the situation escalated and how you would act now with all the right tools in hand. Always make use of your experiences and so trick yourself into reliving situations to unlearn some of the bad habits you had developed. Be careful not to take these scenarios to extremes as this will lead the experience to crash and crumble if not well balanced by your observant self. Accept those feelings, they are natural reactions, and if you face them with love and objectivity, you will be able to understand them, acknowledge that you have felt or feel pain at this moment, then follow it with weighing your options.

Living a life in balance is not a goal; it requires constant effort to balance out!

THANK YOU FOR READING

If you enjoyed the book, we ask that you leave us
an honest review to help others to help us spread
this positive message far and wide.

You can leave your review on our Amazon listing here.

www.amazon.com/dp/B0BC4PJ3SK

If you would like to know more about
THE BALANCE Luxury Rehab where Abdullah
practices the methods you have just read,
you can find us here:

www.thebalance.rehab

Abdullah is the founder and CEO of THE BALANCE Luxury Rehab. Holding two master's degrees, one in General Management and one in Business Engineering from the University of St. Gallen as well as several degrees in Psychology, Integrative Health & Medicine, Nutrition & Food, Cognitive Behavioural Therapy (CBT), Neuro-Linguistic Programming (NLPM), Mindfulness (MBSR), Life Coaching, and Addiction Treatment. He has gained vast know-how in business strategy and change management working on numerous VC/PE/M&A transactions and leading companies in the health & medical services industry. He lives in the countryside with his wife, three children and their many animals.

Printed in Great Britain
by Amazon

43618709R00158